NUMERACY

KEY STAGE 2: YEAR 4/ PRIMARY 5

SUE ATKINSON
DIANA COBDEN

HOPSCOTCH
EDUCATIONAL PUBLISHING

Contents

Published by Hopscotch Educational Publishing Ltd,
Althorpe House, Althorpe Street, Leamington Spa CV31 2AU.

© 1999 Hopscotch Educational Publishing

Written by Sue Atkinson and Diana Cobden
Series design by Blade Communications
Illustrated by Jean de Lemos
Cover illustration by Claire Boyce
Printed by Clintplan, Southam

Sue and Liz Atkinson and Diana Cobden hereby assert their
moral right to be identified as the authors of this work in
accordance with the Copyright, Designs and Patents Act, 1988.

ISBN 1-902239-34-2 372.7 ATK (SOT)

developing
Numeracy
Skills

Numeracy

ABOUT THE SERIES

Developing Numeracy Skills is a series of books aimed at developing the basic skills of the 'Framework for teaching mathematics'. There is one book for each year from Reception (Scottish Primary 1), through Key Stage 1 to the end of Key Stage 2 (Scottish Primary 7).

The series offers a structured approach which provides detailed lesson plans to teach specific numeracy skills. A unique feature of the series is the provision of differentiated photocopiable activities which are aimed at considerably reducing teacher preparation time.

 ## ABOUT THIS BOOK

This book is for teachers of Year 4 children and Scottish level P5. It aims to:

♦ give emphasis to those aspects of numeracy that teachers on the National Numeracy Project found to be crucial to raising the standards of numeracy in their classrooms
♦ support a threefold structured lesson for maximising learning to raise standards
♦ support teachers in developing children's flexible methods of calculating
♦ encourage a wide range of mathematical vocabulary by giving some key questions to ask
♦ support teachers with a wide range of mental maths questions to develop good mental recall with children.

Throughout the book the maths is set in the context of the dinosaurs but you can adapt the lessons by using your own topic.

You will find that the content for the other books for Year 3/P4 to Year 6/P7 in this series is structured in a similar way to assist you if you have a mixed age class. So if you have mixed 7 to 9 year olds, you can use the Y3/P4 book alongside this one in order to develop different lessons that follow on from this book.

 ## CHAPTER CONTENT

 ### Overall learning objectives

Each chapter has two lesson plans and the overall learning objectives outline the aims for both lessons and the further activities in each chapter.

 ### Assessment focus

This sets out the specific learning objective that you will be able to assess for each individual lesson within the chapter. (See page 4 for more on assessment.)

 ### Resources

This is a list of what you will need to do the lessons.

 ### Oral work and mental calculation

This section is a 'mental maths warm up' and can sometimes have a different learning objective from the main lesson plan. It gives you ideas for how to develop quick mental recall with your children, so keeping key ideas ticking over and giving them the extra practice they need to be confident. You can 'mix and match' these to suit your lesson. So, you might want to do multiplication of 7x and 8x every day for a week, even when your main lesson is about measuring, or you might want to recap something about shape and space on a day when the main lesson is about number, and so on. This section of the lesson would be between about five and ten minutes long.

 ### Starting point: whole class

This provides ideas for introducing the activity and may include key questions to ask the children so that they can move on to their group task having been introduced to concepts and the vocabulary they will need for the group activities. This starting point is usually about 10 to 15 minutes long, depending on the task.

Group activities

This explains the tasks that the children will do. The focus group works with you and this group alternates between the different ability groups. The section on 'teacher-independent groups' gives three tasks that can be done more or less independently of you. Sometimes you might use only two of the three independent tasks because one group is the focus group. The group 1 tasks are the easiest and the group 3 tasks the hardest. For Year 4/P5 children, this section is about 15 to 20 minutes long, depending on the task. Some of these teacher-independent tasks are maths games. Games give plenty of practice with the learning objective, help children to learn the language associated with the concept you are teaching, and can provide the incentive to keep working while you are busy with your focus group.

 ## Using the differentiated activity sheets

Activity 1 is for the children who are likely to struggle with the content of the lesson and who need a simple task, often with lower numbers than other groups. Activity 2 is for children who seem to have grasped the main ideas during the whole-class starter, and Activity 3 for those who need a more challenging task.

The book symbol at the bottom of some activity pages is for further work to be done in maths books.

 ## Plenary session

This suggests ideas for a whole-class review to discuss the learning outcomes and gives questions to ask so that children have a chance to reflect on what they have learned and for the teacher to assess. This section is usually about five to ten minutes.

 ## Further activities

This is a list of further activities that can be developed from the lessons to give children more experience with the learning objectives. Some of these use generic sheets at the back of the book and some could be used for homework.

 ## Extension

These are ideas for how to take children further on and give them more difficult tasks.

 ## Support

These are ideas for children who are going to need more support before they have grasped the learning objectives.

 ## The use of calculators

Children will not be using calculators for mental calculations unless the intention is to free them from the time it takes to calculate when your objective is that they need to see a pattern. So, if you want the children to see the pattern of multiplying by 10, doing this on a calculator will teach them an enormous amount about place value that they might not learn from using an abacus, for example. Calculators are invaluable tools for teaching maths, just as cubes and place value boards are, but we must teach children to use them well. It is not a good use of calculators to use them repeatedly for checking, though this can be useful at times. Children need to check their work by doing the calculation in a different way, not resorting to keying in the numbers.

 ## GENERIC SHEETS

There are some generic sheets at the back of the book that give extra help with key skills and can also be made into maths games. These sheets can be photocopied and adapted to suit your different groups. Guidance on using them is given in the lesson plans or in the Further activities section.

 ## ASSESSMENT

You will notice at the top of each activity sheet there is a row of three small boxes. These link with your assessment of how well the child has grasped the intended learning for that lesson. On page 5 there is a list of the assessment criteria for both lessons for each chapter. (Those for the activity sheets are in italics.) You can use these criteria to decide how well a child has grasped the content of a particular lesson.

4
©Hopscotch Educational Publishing

developing
Numeracy
Skills

Numeracy
Year 4/P5

+ If they seem not to have grasped the concept, tick the first box.
+ If there is evidence of the child having learned what you intended, tick the second box.
+ Tick the third box for children who have a very secure grasp of the lesson and you think can use and apply the concept.

Of course, there will often be no evidence on the sheet that corresponds with your observations of some children's understanding during oral maths time and when you work with your focus group. You will need to make a note (on the sheet if you want) of what those children said or did to back up why you ticked a particular box. We need to listen to children very carefully as they respond to the activity and we need to use prompting and probing questions in order to be clear about what each individual understands. Assessment is much broader than children's recordings, so your additional annotations based on your observations are important. At the end of each half term, flicking through each child's sheets can give you a basis for your teacher assessments, and will enable you to plan for your next half term.

In addition to this assessment on the children's sheets, there is a self-assessment sheet on page 96. The blank spaces are for you and the child to record specific targets that the child has achieved. The children will need to reflect on their learning; for example, they need to think of a favourite way to add 2-digit numbers and think about what they would like to be better at in maths.

Year 4 Assessment Criteria

Chapter 1
Can the children read and write numbers to 10 000, add and subtract 1, 10, 100, and 1000 to or from any whole number?
Can they round up and down to the nearest 10 or 100?

Chapter 2
Can they compare and order numbers?
Can they multiply and divide whole numbers by 10?

Chapter 3
Can they recognise and extend number sequences?
Can they make general statements about number patterns?

Chapter 4
Can they use the vocabulary of addition and subtraction to solve problems?
Can they use partitioning for addition and subtraction calculations?

Chapter 5
Can they add or subtract to the nearest multiple of 10 and adjust?
Can they understand that although addition can be done in any order, this does not work for subtraction?

Chapter 6
Can they explain their chosen method for a calculation and start to make jottings of their mental methods?
Can they select appropriate methods for a range of calculations?

Chapter 7
Can they solve multiplication and division problems using known facts?
Can they explain and use the relationship between multiplication and division?

Chapter 8
Can they use multiplication and division to solve problems using a range of vocabulary?
Can they check their work using different strategies?

Chapter 9
Can they recognise and use equivalent fractions?
Can they explain that division is used to find fractions of numbers?

Chapter 10
Can they identify and use equivalent decimals and fractions?
Can they work with decimal fractions and put them in order?

Chapter 11
Can they solve mathematical problems and explain their methods?
Can they make general statements and describe what they have done?

Chapter 12
Can they use linear measuring equipment with increasing accuracy?
Can they measure and calculate area and perimeter, then make generalisations about them?

Chapter 13
Can they use a variety of capacity measuring equipment and read different capacity scales?
Can they read different clocks and solve problems involving time?

Chapter 14
Can they extract information from and interpret graphs and tables?
Can they devise a question, collect data and present it appropriately, making interpretations and predictions?

The criteria in italics are those that relate to the children's activity sheets.

Numeracy
Year 4/P5

developing
Numeracy
Skills

5

©Hopscotch Educational Publishing

Number line counting

 Overall learning objectives

- Add and subtract, 1, 10, 100 and 1000.
- Count on and back in 1s, 10s, 100s and 1000s from 1-, 2-, 3- and 4-digit numbers.
- Use the vocabulary of estimation and approximation.
- Round 2- and 3-digit numbers to the nearest 10 or 100.

LESSON ONE
WHAT DO YOU KNOW?

 Assessment focus

Can the children read and write numbers to 10 000 and add and subtract 1, 10, 100 and 1000 to or from any whole number?

 Resources

- 4-spike abacus with beads
- place value cards, 0–9, 10–90, 100–900 and 1000–9000

 Oral work and mental calculation

Properties of numbers

- Tell the children you are thinking of a number and they must find what it is by asking mathematical questions but the only answer you will give is 'yes' or 'no'. Give examples, such as, *"Is it in the 2 times table?"* and *"Is it greater than 10?"* Start with lower numbers and write the number's properties on the board. Once they are confident, let them work in groups of four, taking turns to think of the number. Share some examples and discuss good questions.

 Starting point: whole class

- Using a 4-spike abacus marked with thousands, hundreds, tens and ones (units), show a 2-digit number, such as 63. Ask for a volunteer to write it on the board, saying what each digit represents. Add a bead to show 163 and ask for the new number to be written. Can the children say what has been changed? Add another hundreds bead, asking them to say what has happened. Continue by adding thousands beads. Remove all the beads from the abacus, write a number on the board and ask a child to show this on the abacus. Repeat with other numbers, each time asking them to say the value of the digits and what will change if a multiple of 10 or 1 is added or subtracted.
- Show what each of the digits in a 4-digit number, such as 2475, represents: 2 thousands, 4 hundreds, 7 tens and 5 ones. Leave the abacus pictures and the words, thousands, hundreds, tens and ones, on the board for group 1 to refer to.

 Group activities

 Focus group

Assess the children's abilities to use numbers up to 10 000. They use the place value cards to make a 2-, 3- or 4-digit number (depending on the ability of the group). In turn can they say their number and the value of each digit? Ask each one to count on or back in 10s, 100s or 1000s until you say *"Stop"* and to make the last number with their cards. Can they work out how many multiples were counted on or back each time? Pose questions for them to work out using their cards, such as *"Make 1674 with your cards. What must you add to make 8674?"* Establish whether they can write some of the numbers in words.

 Teacher-independent groups

Activity sheet 1: These children may need an abacus to model answers on as they complete the sheet. They might need reminding that when adding 1, 10 or 100, they use the start number each time.

Number line counting

Activity sheet 2: This group is asked to partition numbers into thousands, hundreds, tens and ones and to consider a rule for adding or subtracting 100.

Activity sheet 3: This is the same as for group 2 except that they are asked to add or subtract multiples of 10, 100 or 1000.

✦ *Plenary session*

✦ Ask the children what they have learned about adding and subtracting 1, 10, 100 or 1000. Write a number on the board and discuss the effect of adding or subtracting any multiple of 10. Finish by asking the children, in pairs, to make numbers with place value cards that are for example: 100 more than 199; 10 more than 77; 200 less than 624 and so on.

✦ ✦ ✦ ✦ ✦ ✦

◆ LESSON TWO
TO THE NEAREST 10

✦ *Assessment focus*

Can children round up and down to the nearest 10 or 100?

✦ *Resources*

- ✦ paper and pencil for the oral activity
- ✦ till receipts
- ✦ 1–9 cards
- ✦ place value cards
- ✦ a washing line

✦ *Oral work and mental calculation*

Odd and even numbers

✦ Write a 2-digit number on the board. Ask if it is odd or even and how they know. Say that they will be writing chains of numbers using the rule that if a number is odd, 1 is added and if it is even, it is halved such as in the example below.

✦ ✦ ✦ ✦ ✦ ✦

✦ A chain ends when it gets to 1. Try an even number example. Tell the children to use 1–9 cards to make a 2-digit number and to write the chain, then to reverse the two digits and make another 2-digit number, for example 26 and 62, then find the second chain. Discuss the endings and lengths of number chains. Do larger numbers give longer chains?

✦ *Starting point: whole class*

✦ On a 'washing line' attach the multiples of 5 from 0–100. Divide the class into two groups and provide 1-9 and 10-90 place value cards placed face down. One person from each group turns over one of each card and makes a 2-digit number. Each player writes their number on paper, pins it to the line in the correct position and says which is the nearest multiple of 10. Ask the children if they can remember what happens to multiples of 5. They may suggest they are rounded either up or down so tell them these numbers are usually rounded up to the next 10. The player who is nearest scores 1 point for their team. If both are the same distance away they score 1 point each.

$$45 \xrightarrow{+1} 46 \xrightarrow{\div 2} 23 \xrightarrow{+1} 24 \xrightarrow{\div 2} 12 \xrightarrow{\div 2} 6 \xrightarrow{\div 2} 3 \xrightarrow{+1} 4 \xrightarrow{\div 2} 2 \xrightarrow{\div 2} 1$$

Number line counting

◆ Group activities

Focus group

Tell the children that if you have only a few things in your basket in the shop you often work out about how much the bill will come to by rounding the prices up or down. Have a small collection of toys or games marked with prices that can be rounded up or down to the nearest £ or 10p. Ask what the rounded prices will be and add these to the labels on the items. Work with the group to show how much quicker it is to add prices in this way and work out the cost of multiples, for example 3 games costing £1.99 each. Give them some old till receipts and ask them to write all the prices to the nearest £ and then to the nearest 10p.

Teacher-independent groups

Group 1: This group continues to play the whole-class starter game in pairs, with the player who makes a number nearest to a multiple of 10 scoring the point.

Group 2: Again this group plays the game from the starter activity in pairs using place value cards to make 3-digit numbers. The numbers are rounded to the nearest 10 and a record is kept of the new numbers.

Group 3: Again this group plays the starter activity game in pairs using place value cards to make 3-digit numbers. The player whose number is closest to a multiple of 100 scores 2 and the player with the number closest to a multiple of 10 scores 1. They should keep a record of their numbers.

My number	My number rounded to the nearest 100	My number rounded to the nearest 10
376	400	380

◆ Plenary session

- ◆ Ask the focus group to share how they were rounding prices and say why this can be useful.
- ◆ Write up some prices that can easily be rounded to the nearest £ and ask the children to work out the approximate cost of several items, for example *"A ball costs £2.95. About how much will three cost?"* Ask how they can use this to work out the exact cost. Expect some children to state that 15p can then be subtracted from £9.00. Show how the same process can be used for calculations such as 5 x 195 and 297 x 4.

◆ Further activities

- ◆ Play Place Invaders using decimals, for example *"Change 625.7 into 625.1, or 626.9"*.
- ◆ Give the children a container of mixed coins. Working in pairs, each child takes a handful and counts how much they have. The player with an amount of money nearest to a multiple of £1 scores 5 points. The player with money nearest to a multiple of 10p scores 2 points. So, if the two amounts are 86p and 79p the player with 86p scores 5 and the one with 79p scores 2.

◆ Extension

- ◆ The children could find examples of large numbers being used in reference books, such as about world records or space. They can round them to the nearest multiple of 10, 100 and so on.

◆ Support

- ◆ Cut an A4 sheet of card in half. Make 2 different cylinders (tall/thin, short/fat). Estimate to the nearest 10 how many 2cm cubes each will hold. Then count the cubes and round them.

✦ What's it worth? ✦

1. Write the numbers.

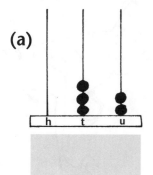 (a)

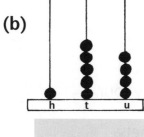 (b)

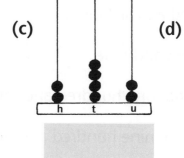 (c)

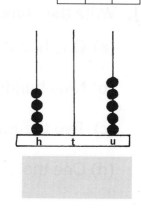 (d)

2. Draw the beads.

```
  h   t   u
    2 9
```

```
  h   t   u
   2 3 1
```

```
  h   t   u
   5 2 0
```

```
  h   t   u
   4 0 8
```

3.

 +1　　　　　 +10　　　　　 +100

		+1	+10	+100
(a)	28	29	38	128
(b)	33		43	
(c)	167			
(d)	324			

Write 3 more numbers.

_____ _____ _____ _____

_____ _____ _____ _____

_____ _____ _____ _____

 Use ⬚3⬚ ⬚8⬚ ⬚4⬚ to make some 3-digit numbers.
Write your numbers in words.

◆ What's it worth? ◆

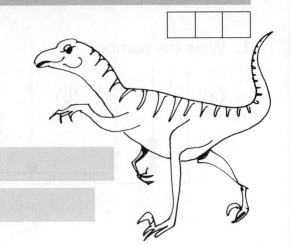

1. Write the numbers.

   (a) One hundred and sixty four ▢

   (b) Nine hundred and nine ▢

   (c) Two thousand, one hundred and forty four ▢

   (d) One thousand, nine hundred and ninety ▢

2. Write the numbers in words.
   (a) 376 _____

   (b) 804 _____

   (c) 1111 _____

   (d) 3609 _____

3. Write the missing numbers.

   (example)   1 3 6 2   =   1 0 0 0   +   3 0 0   +   6 0   +   2

   (a)   2 4 1 3   =   2 0 0 0   +   ____   +   1 0   +   3

   (b)   5 6 3 7   =   ____   +   6 0 0   +   __   +   7

   (c)   8 7 5 5   =   8 0 0 0   +   ____   +   __   +   __

   Write 2 more.

   ____   ____   ____   ____

   ____   ____   ____   ____

4. **(a)**   374 – 100 =   **(b)**   872 + 100 =

   (c)   1539 + 100 =   **(d)**   9236 – 100 =

   (e)   2886 + ____ = 2986   **(f)**   3835 – ____ = 3535

 Using ▢2 ▢5 ▢6 ▢7 , make some 4-digit numbers. Add 100 to your numbers. Subtract 100 from your numbers. What is your rule?

✦ **What's it worth?** ✦

1. Write the numbers.

(a) Two thousand, nine hundred

(b) Six thousand, three hundred and sixty two

(c) One thousand, two hundred and four

(d) Nine thousand and ten

2. Write the numbers in words.

(a) 1112 _____

(b) 6074 _____

(c) 7908 _____

(d) 2003 _____

3. Complete the boxes.

(a) $144 = 100 + \boxed{} + 4$ (b) $769 = \boxed{} + 60 + 9$

(c) $6372 = 6000 + \boxed{} + 70 + 2$

(d) $1720 = 1000 + \boxed{} + \boxed{} + 0$

Do 3 more on the back of this sheet

4. Write the missing numbers.

(a) $374 + \boxed{} = 474$ (b) $963 - \boxed{} = 933$

(c) $1979 - 700 = \boxed{}$ (d) $6330 + 300 = \boxed{}$

(e) $9206 - \boxed{} = 7206$ (f) $2866 + \boxed{} = 3066$

 Using $\boxed{7}\ \boxed{2}\ \boxed{3}\ \boxed{4}$, make some 4-digit numbers. Add 1000 to your numbers. Subtract 1000 from your numbers. What is your rule?

developing Numeracy Skills

Place value

Overall learning objectives

+ Use the symbols > < and = between two given numbers.
+ Use the vocabulary of place value.
+ Order sets of numbers, including decimals.
+ Say what a digit represents when using whole numbers and decimals.
+ Multiply and divide whole numbers by 10.

LESSON ONE
PUT IT IN PLACE

Assessment focus

Can the children compare and order numbers?

Resources

+ 0–9 cards
+ place value cards, 10–90, 100–900
+ base 10 equipment and Th T H U boards

Oral work and mental calculation

Calculating time

+ Give the children practice at mental calculation of time by asking questions such as:
  "It is a quarter to 10. How long is it until playtime, …lunchtime, …home time?"
  "I leave home at 7.30am and arrive at school 25 minutes later. What time do I arrive?"
  "A train journey takes 3 and a half hours. If the train leaves at 10.15am when does it arrive?"
+ Ask the children to write the times on the board. They might suggest either analogue or digital methods, so discuss the different ways of writing time. The times can also be shown on a clock face. Write some times on the board and ask the children to add and subtract 30 minutes from each of them, then share answers with a partner. Give a variety of times to cater for differing abilities.

Starting point: whole class

+ In advance of the lesson prepare two strips of card joined to a larger piece of card by paper fasteners, such as below.

+ These strips can be used to show the equal, greater and less than symbols.
+ Ask six children to turn over two, three or four of their 0–9 cards to make numbers in the 10s, 100s or 1000s and to write them on card. See if the children can peg the numbers in order, from smallest to largest, on a 'washing line' and give reasons for their decisions about position. Six more children can make numbers and add these to the line. Read the numbers together forwards and backwards in order of size.
+ Take pairs of the numbers, hold them up and ask which way the symbol should be written to denote the smaller, larger, or equality of the numbers. Write the pairs of numbers and appropriate symbol on the board to assist the groups later. Continue by giving a number and symbol and asking children to give a number that will make the number statement correct, for example ☐ > 105. Some children have difficulty in remembering the way round to write the symbols, so say one way to remember is that it is like a dinosaur's mouth opening towards the larger number.

Group activities

 Focus group

Work with this group to find midpoint values between two numbers on a number line. Start with a pair of children each taking a card from a 10–90 place value set of numbers. Write one at each end of a number line.

30   50

Place value

Ask the children for the number that comes halfway. Another two children take a card each from the 100-900 set of numbers and repeat. Once the children are confident one partner takes a card from each set and the other makes a number that is 20 more or less, then finds the midpoints between these numbers. Tell the pairs to make more numbers with a small difference and find the halfway points on an empty number line.

 Teacher-independent groups

Activity sheet 1: The children doing this sheet may find ordering numbers easier if they write them on pieces of paper and move them around until they are confident with the order. The numbers on the sheet have been kept to values that can be checked on a number line.

Activity sheet 2: The numbers for this group to order are more challenging and closer in value. Suggest they discuss the order with a partner to share ideas.

Activity sheet 3: The numbers here are even more challenging.

 Plenary session

✦ Let the children explain their decisions for ordering numbers. Discuss the significant figures when ordering. Write up some 4-digit numbers with a common numeral in different positions, such as 4598, 2752, 5631 and 8725. Ask for the value of the 5 in each.

LESSON TWO
BIG AND SMALL NUMBERS

 Assessment focus

Can the children multiply and divide whole numbers by 10?

 Resources

✦ base 10 equipment
✦ generic sheet 4 (page 93)

 Oral work and mental calculation

Multiplication strategies

✦ Write 6 x 7 on the board and ask if any of the children can remember the 6x table. Write the answer. Say you want them to find different ways of working out the answer, using number facts they know. Ask which tables they know well (these will probably be 2x, 5x and 10x) and then ask for

suggestions of how to use these tables to work out 6 x 7. For example, the 7 can be split into 2 and 5, making the calculation (6 x 2) + (6 x 5). Give a few minutes for pairs to find a method and write some on the board, discussing the different ways. Ask the class to use one of the methods to calculate 6 x 17 and 6 x 27. Again share strategies.

 Starting point: whole class

✦ Display a large place value board. Put 5 in the ones column and multiply it by 10 a few times to show how the number moves left across the board. The rule **isn't** to add a zero! Repeat this with 2- and 3-digit numbers, then start with 5000 and show the effect of dividing by 10.

thousands 1000	hundreds 100	tens 10	ones 1	
			5	
	500	50		x 10
5000				x 10
				x 10

Explain the rules of '4-in-a-row' (generic sheet 4) ready for the group activities. (See page 14.)

Place value

 ◆ Group activities

Focus group

With the children's help build up this chart, using a place value board and base 10 equipment, if necessary:

1	2	3	4	5	6	7	8	9
10	20	30	40	50	60	70	80	90
100	200	300	400	500	600	700	800	900
1000	2000	3000	4000	5000	6000	7000	8000	9000

Can they explain the effect of multiplying by 10 and by 10 again, or if a number is divided by 10 twice? An able group can explore dividing the single digit numbers by 10 to get decimals. Point to various numbers and ask for the answer they are multiplied or divided by 10. Ask questions such as *"How many tens in 100?"* or *"How many 300s in 3000?"* Establish rules for multiplying and dividing by 10.

 Teacher-independent groups

Group 1: Use generic sheet 4 to prepare a '4-in-a-row' game with single digit numbers or multiples of 10 to be multiplied or divided.

Group 2: This group works in pairs and uses generic sheet 4 to make a '4-in-a-row' game using 2- and 3-digit multiples of 10, such as 610, 60, 2100, 20, 210.

Group 3: This group should make harder games involving multiplication and division of higher numbers by 10 and 1.

 ◆ Plenary session

◆ Display the chart made by the focus group. Ask them to explain what they did and found out. Expect them to be able to explain that multiplying or dividing by 10 and then 10 again is the same as x or ÷ 100.

◆ Ask for suggestions about multiplying or dividing numbers by 20, such as multiplying by 10 and doubling. Try some examples together.

 ◆ Further activities

◆ Pairs of children need three shuffled sets of 0–9 cards placed face down on the table and a game board each:

One at a time they turn over a card and place it on the game board with the aim of making a number as near to 10 000 as possible. The nearest is the winner.

 ◆ Extension

◆ Use an extended version of the '4-in-a-row' game using decimal numbers, such as the one shown opposite.

 ◆ Support

◆ Give these children some practical work with bundles of straws, linked paperclips and so on.

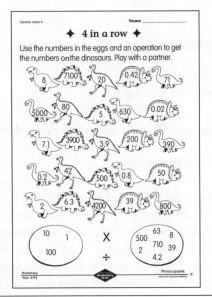

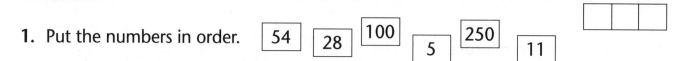

✦ All in order ✦

1. Put the numbers in order.   54   28   100   5   250   11

smallest   largest

2. Now do these.   99   63   19   46   66   83

largest   smallest

3. Put the signs in the boxes.

    > greater than   < less than   = equals

(a)   10 ☐ 11   **(b)**   16 ☐ 15

(c)   20 ☐ 19 + 1   **(d)**   18 ☐ 28

(e)   100 ☐ 90   **(f)**   10 ☐ 100

4. Write the number to make these true.

(a)   20 > ☐   **(b)**   20 < ☐

(c)   15 > ☐   **(d)**   15 < ☐

(e)   100 > ☐   **(f)**   100 < ☐

Write 3 more.

   Make 6 2-digit numbers and put them in order. Go from smallest to largest. Make 6 more numbers and order them from largest to smallest.

developing Numeracy Skills

©Hopscotch Educational Publishing

✦ All in order ✦

1. Put the numbers in order.

235   54   39   115   86   1256   55

smallest   largest

2. Now do these.

129   84   101   2365   876   8766   21

largest   smallest

3. Use these signs between the numbers.

> greater than   < less than   = equals

(a) 36 ☐ 49   **(b)** 136 ☐ 186 – 50   **(c)** 94 ☐ 74

(d) 88 ☐ 81   **(e)** 1866 ☐ 86   **(f)** 100 ☐ 110

4. Write the number to make these true.

(a) 21 > ☐   **(b)** 163 < ☐   **(c)** 88 = ☐

(d) 635 > ☐   **(e)** 5622 < ☐   **(f)** 8399 > ☐

5.   Tyrannosaurus (14m)   Diplodocus (23m)   Triceratops (9m)

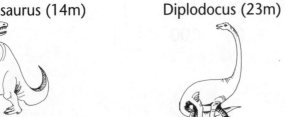

Which is longest? _____   Which is shortest? _____

   Make pairs of numbers with 2 of your 0–9 cards.
Use >, < or = between them.

Name _____

✦ All in order ✦

1. Put the numbers in order. 379 167 277 284 644 369 384

smallest   largest

2. Now do these. 1096 2437 196 2344 9907 2766 5378

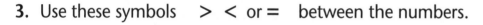

largest   smallest

3. Use these symbols > < or = between the numbers.

(a) 49 ☐ 52   (b) 316 ☐ 5   (c) 963 ☐ 763 + 200

(d) 754 ☐ 483   (e) 3361 ☐ 999   (f) 1926 ☐ 1962

Write 3 more like this.

_____   _____   _____

4. Write the number to make these correct.

(a) 59 > ☐   (b) 877 < ☐   (c) 88 = ☐

5.   Triceratops (9m)   Tyrannosaurus (14m)   Diplodocus (23m)   Stegosaurus (10m)

Which is longest? _____ Which is shortest? _____

   Make pairs of numbers with 2 of your 0–9 cards.
Use >, < or = between them.

Chapter 3

Properties of numbers

 Overall learning objectives

- Identify and predict number patterns and sequences.
- Identify and make general statements about odd and even numbers to 1000.
- Recognise and extend number sequences, including those going beyond zero.
- Recognise negative numbers on a number line.
- Use knowledge of sums or products of odd/even numbers.

LESSON ONE
WHAT COMES NEXT?

 Assessment focus

Can the children recognise and extend number sequences?

 Resources

- large and individual 1–100 squares (generic sheets 1 and 2 – pages 90–91)
- number lines, including some with negative values
- place value cards
- dice

 Oral work and mental calculation

Approximate answers

- Display a 0–100 number line. Say some 2-digit numbers and ask individual children to come and circle them on the line. Discuss which multiple of 10 each one is nearest. Write a calculation on the board, such as 18 + 34 and ask the children to round both numbers to the nearest 10, to give 20 + 30, and find the answer. Compare the approximate with the actual answer. Tell them to work in pairs, using 0–9 cards to make a 2-digit number each and add them by rounding to the nearest 10 then comparing this with the exact

answer. After a few examples have been tried discuss how close the approximations were to the exact answers. Tell them this is a useful way of checking whether answers are about right.

 Starting point: whole class

- Write a sequence of numbers on the board:
      5   10   15   20   25 …
- Ask "What are the next three numbers in this sequence? How do you know?" Write another sequence:
      1   4   7   10   13 …
  and ask the same questions. Use larger numbers:
      175   200   225   250   275 …
- Ask "Now what about this one …?"
      12   9   6   3   0 …
- Ask them to put up their hands if they think they know the answer. If someone suggests negative numbers ask for an explanation. Draw a zero to –10 number line on the board, showing how the numbers go back from zero. Practise counting from zero to –10 and back again. Write a sequence starting from a negative value and ask children to extend it, giving reasons for their choice. Finally, write a sequence that does not have the same size of step:
      6   13   19   26   32 …

Show how it can help to write the size of step:

6   +7   13   +6   19   +7   26   +6   32

 Group activities

Focus group

Use –10 to +30 number lines (these can be made by the children). Give them a place for starting a sequence, the size of step and the direction along the line. Ask them to start writing the sequence then predict, then test, the next few numbers. Sequences can start or end with negative values. Once they are confident, they can decide on a starting number and direction and throw a dice for the size of step.

Properties of numbers

Teacher-independent groups

Activity sheet 1: The sequences of numbers on this sheet are based mainly on familiar number patterns such as odd/even numbers and multiples of 5 and 10. The steps between each number in the sequences are the same size. To help them generate their own sequences they will need number lines or squares. Encourage the group to talk about the numbers in the sequences, especially the effect of using steps of 5 from different starting points.

Activity sheet 2: This group will benefit from being able to use positive to negative 10 number lines both to find the next numbers and to generate their own sequences.

Activity sheet 3: This is the same as Activity sheet 2, but uses different sizes of step within a sequence. The answers to the questions on this sheet are: 1a) +9; 1b) –4; 1c) +100; 4) –2.

 Plenary session

✦ Invite the independent groups to share some of their own sequences, asking the other children what the next numbers will be. Some of group 3 may be able to predict, for example, what the 10th number in a sequence will be, for example 3, 13, 23…
✦ *"What did you enjoy in maths today?"*
✦ *"What did you find difficult?"*

LESSON TWO
IS THERE A PATTERN?

 Assessment focus

Can the children make general statements about number patterns?

 Resources

✦ 100 squares – generic sheets 1 and 2 (pages 90–91)

 Oral work and mental calculation

Giving change

✦ It might help to display a 100 square. Give the children practice at working out change as quickly as possible, and sharing strategies. Tell them that you will say amounts of money and they must work out the change from £1. Keep the numbers to multiples of 10p initially and then use multiples of 5p. Gradually use amounts between the multiples of 5 and 10 and ask the class to give change from

amounts other than £1. Discuss how to give change using the shopkeeper's method. For example, to find the change from 40p for an item costing 28p, they might add 2p to make 30p and add 10p to make 40p. Round off the session by working some of these out with the whole class.

Starting point: whole class

✦ Display a large 100 square. Ask for examples of a pattern or sequence on the square. They may suggest the multiples of 10, 5 and 2, so ask how these can be described and if the next numbers beyond 100 can be predicted.
✦ Ask someone to start crossing out every multiple of 3, up to 30. What pattern do these numbers make? Can the number of multiples of 3 up to 100 can be predicted? Show how a number sequence is generated by adding the first and last numbers in each row, such as 1 + 10 = 11, 11 + 20 = 31 and 21 + 30 = 51.
✦ Tell the groups they will be working with different sized squares and draw a 4 x 4 grid to demonstrate what you mean, saying that this is the size group 1 will use.

1	2	③	4
5	⑥	7	8
⑨	10	11	⑫
13	14	⑮	16

Properties of numbers

✦ With the help of the class identify some number patterns. Can they spot the multiples of 3 and 5, and describe the pattern? Write some of the ideas on the board to help group 1 get started.

◆ Group activities

Focus group

Continue to work with the patterns on a 100 square. Ask them to put cubes or counters on different multiples, describe the patterns they make and predict how these would continue on a 101–200 square. Ask the children to find the multiples of 9 and 11, describe the pattern and see if they can identify why these make a diagonal line, going either from right to left or vice versa. Encourage the children to consider how to record the number patterns and sequences they find. Take the opportunity to assess the children's ability to describe patterns and make predictions.

Teacher-independent groups

Group 1: Working with the 4 x 4 square, this group should continue to identify patterns and sequences

of numbers, using the work done in the whole-class starter activity as their starting point. Encourage them to discuss and record their patterns.

Group 2: Again, following on from the introduction, this group should identify, record and predict patterns and sequences, this time based on a 5 x 5 grid (using numbers 1–25).

Group 3: This group should do the same activities as groups 1 and 2 but using a 6 x 6 grid.

◆ Plenary session

✦ Draw the 5 x 5 and 6 x 6 grids on the board. Invite members of each group to talk about some of the number patterns they have found. Show how each size of grid has the multiples of that number down the right side and ask what would happen with grids of other sizes.
✦ Ask the focus group to share their findings about the multiples of 9 and 11. The others might find something similar about their grids.
✦ Find out if there are any generalisations to be made if the first and last numbers of each row in a grid are added. For example, in a 6 x 6 grid, 1 + 6 = 7, 7 + 12 = 19, so the difference is 12, which is twice the row length.

◆ Further activities

✦ Explore other patterns and sequences in number squares. For example, count on in steps of the same size using different starting points and describing the outcomes.
✦ Use a 100 square and find the pattern of numbers whose digits add to 9. For example, adding the digits of 27 makes 9. The children should describe the pattern and say what they notice about the numbers.

◆ Extension

✦ Make generalisations about the number sequences in any sized square. For example, in

any sized square the multiples of that number are on the right; the number sequence minus 1 goes diagonally from right to left; and the number sequence plus one goes diagonally from left to right.

◆ Support

✦ On a 100 square, put a cube on all the numbers with a 3 in them. What pattern do they make? Put the cubes on numbers with a 9 in them. What is the pattern now? Try other numbers. Explain the patterns.

20
©Hopscotch Educational Publishing

developing
Numeracy
Skills

Numeracy
Year 4/P5

✦ What's the rule? ✦

Write the missing numbers.

1. (11) (13) (   ) (17) (   ) (   ) (23)

    The rule is _____

2. (20) (22) (   ) (   ) (28) (   ) (   )

    The rule is _____

3. (29) (27) (   ) (23) (   ) (   ) (   )

    The rule is _____

4. (10) (   ) (30) (   ) (   ) (60) (   )

    The rule is _____

5. (100) (90) (   ) (   ) (60) (   ) (   )

    The rule is _____

6. (0) (   ) (10) (   ) (20) (   ) (30)

    The rule is _____

7. (6) (11) (   ) (   ) (26) (   ) (   )

    The rule is _____

Choose a start number.
Write a +5 pattern.

_____

Choose more start numbers and write some +5 and −5 patterns.
What do you notice about them?

developing
Numeracy
Skills

◆ What's the rule? ◆

1. Write the missing numbers.

a)
36   46   76

b) 99   69   49

Write your own sequence like this.

Start

2. Try these sequences.

a)
3   8   23   43

b) 56   46   31

What is the rule for these sequences? _____

3. Here are some harder sequences.

a) 353   357   369

What is the rule? _____

b) 11   9   3   –3

What is the rule? _____

c) 10   4   –5

What do you think comes next? _____

 Make a 2-digit number with your cards. This is your start number.
Throw a dice for the size of step. Write your sequence going back
as far as you can.

✦ What's the rule? ✦

1. Write the missing numbers.

a)   24 33 60

What is the rule? _____

b)      141 133 121

What did you do this time? _____

c)    82 382 582

What is this rule? _____

2. Make a start number with 0–9 cards. Write a +5 sequence.

What is this number pattern? _____

3. Make a new start number. Write a –5 sequence.

What do you notice about this pattern? _____
Why do you think this happens? _____

4. Finish this sequence and write the rule.

       –7 –3 +1

_____

 Make a set of cards from –10 to +10. Shuffle them. Turn over 6. Put them in order. Do this six times. Make a sequence for your friend to solve.

Addition and subtraction – 1

 ## Overall learning objectives

✦ Consolidate understanding of + and -, and the relationship between them.
✦ Use the vocabulary of addition and subtraction to solve problems.
✦ Use partitioning to work out calculations.
✦ Add/subtract nearest multiples of 10, 100 or 1000 and adjust.
✦ Use number facts and place value to + or – numbers mentally.

LESSON ONE WHICH IS IT?

 ## Assessment focus

Can children use the vocabulary of addition and subtraction to solve problems?

 ## Resources

✦ money – real coins, if possible
✦ place value cards, 1–9, 10–90, 100–900
✦ place value boards
✦ base 10 equipment

 ## Oral work and mental calculation

Addition and subtraction strategies

✦ Write up 35 + 39. *"Who can come and show me the answer?"* Can the children explain how they worked it out? They may see this as double 35 + 4 or (40 + 35) –1 and so on. *"If you know that 35 + 39 = 74 what else do you know?"* (39 + 35 = 74, 74 – 39 = 35 and 74 – 35 = 39.) Write a subtraction and ask them to work out the answer as quickly as possible and then give the other three facts. Continue doing this with a mix of addition and subtraction questions to stress the relationship.

 ## Starting point: whole class

✦ *"The Dinosaur Museum had 165 visitors on Monday. There were 40 more visitors on Tuesday, so how many people visited then?"* Pose this question and ask the children how to solve it. Stress that there were more visitors on Tuesday, so what operation is used? Write the calculation: 165 + 40 = 205. Continue by saying *"45 of the 165 visitors on Monday were children, so how many adults?"* What operation is used this time? Write it down.
✦ Pose similar questions where decisions about the operation must be made and include examples of multi-step operations. For example, *"A box of model dinosaurs had 20 models on the top layer and 20 on the bottom layer. If 12 were sold from the top layer, how many dinosaurs were left?"* Tell the groups that they will be solving problems where they must decide whether to add or subtract and that some problems will include money. To help group 1, write up some of the vocabulary, such as 'more' and 'fewer' with the operation.

 ## Group activities

 Focus group

Display a list of items that might be sold in the museum shop, with their prices. Tell this group that together you are going to write some questions based on the prices and find the answers. They need to decide how to do each question and explain what they did. Will they use addition or subtraction? Talk about what makes a good question. Give them an example. In turns, they should think of a question and write it up. The group then writes the answers with the explanations of what they did. Depending on the ability of the group, money might need to be available.

 Teacher-independent groups

Activity sheet 1: All the 'real-life' problems are single step operations. As some questions involve money the children may need to have this available.

Addition and subtraction – 1

Activity sheet 2: Some two-step operations, involving both addition and subtraction, are included on the sheet.

Activity sheet 3: This is similar to Activity sheet 2 but has more two-step operations.

LESSON TWO SPLIT IT UP

✦ Assessment focus

Can the children use partitioning for addition and subtraction calculations?

✦ Resources

✦ money (plastic or real)
✦ base 10 equipment
✦ place value boards and cards

✦ Oral work and mental calculation

Addition and value of money

✦ Ask some children to come up and write the values of all the coins we use on the board. This will reinforce everyone's knowledge of our coins and will also be a visual aid to help the less able. Say *"I have five coins totalling 83p. Which coins do you think I am holding?"* Discuss the options.
✦ Try some other amounts as a class and then ask the children to continue, working in pairs. One person secretly takes some coins, telling their partner the number and sum of the coins and the other partner decides which coins have been taken.
✦ Ask some of the children to share their methods of working.

✦ Plenary session

✦ Ask pairs of children from each group to tell the class about one of their problems and explain what they did to solve it. Which problems were the most difficult to solve and why was this? Can they explain the clues they used in the solution of problems?

✦ Starting point: whole class

✦ Write up on the board 129 = 100 + 20 + 9. Model this on a place value board with base 10 equipment, explaining that this is called partitioning. Write another number and ask someone to partition it on the place value board and write up the values. Next write:

$$
\begin{array}{l}
1\,2\,5 = 100{+}20{+}5 \\
+\,3\,1\,4 = 300{+}10{+}4
\end{array}
\qquad
\begin{array}{l}
1\,2\,5 = 100{+}20{+}5 \\
+\,3\,1\,4 = \underline{300{+}10{+}4} \\
\text{Which gives:} \quad \underline{400{+}30{+}9}
\end{array}
$$

✦ Ask the children for suggestions for another way of doing this calculation. Show how this can be written as:

$$
\begin{array}{r}
1\,2\,5 \\
+\,3\,1\,4 \\
\hline
4\,0\,0 \\
3\,0 \\
\underline{9} \\
\underline{4\,3\,9}
\end{array}
\qquad
\begin{array}{l}
\text{Show an example} \\
\text{that involves crossing} \\
\text{the tens boundary:}
\end{array}
\qquad
\begin{array}{r}
2\,6\,7 \\
+\,3\,5\,2 \\
\hline
5\,0\,0 \\
1\,1\,0 \\
\underline{9} \\
\underline{6\,1\,9}
\end{array}
$$

✦ Show more examples using the place value boards, including some adding 2-digit to 3-digit numbers, and leave these on the board to help group 1. Explain to the groups how they will be working and recording (although group 1 may need to continue working on calculations like the first example). Emphasise the need to record carefully with the hundreds, tens and ones lined up underneath each other.
✦ Demonstrate how place value cards can be used for partitioning, if necessary.

Addition and subtraction – 1

◆ For the benefit of group 3, show how partitioning can be used for subtraction:

$$3\,2\,5 = 300+20+5$$
$$-\ 2\,1\,4 = \underline{200+10+4}$$
$$\underline{100+10+1}$$

Group activities

Focus group

Use this time to assess whether the children can partition numbers and use this as a strategy for addition and subtraction. On a large sheet of paper write two 2-digit numbers and ask one of the children to partition the numbers then add them. Ask the whole group to make two 2-digit numbers with place value cards. Discuss how they would add these mentally and how they might record the work. Now ask them to add the numbers by partitioning and adding the significant digits first. Talk about the way they worked. The group can continue by making a 2- and a 3-digit number and adding those. Again, discuss the process. If the children are working confidently, give them a set of numbers with different numbers of digits to add, such as 3, 29, 88 and 143. Again stress the need to line up the digits in the right columns.

Teacher-independent groups

Group 1: This group uses place value cards to make a pair of 2-digit numbers. These are modelled on the place value boards and the partitioned numbers are added as was done in the first part of the starting activity. They should record what they did.

Group 2: Using place value cards, these children should make a 2- and a 3-digit number. They add the most significant digits first, as in the second example from the starting point. Place value boards and base 10 equipment should be available if needed. The more confident can progress to adding two 3-digit numbers.

Group 3: Suggest this group starts by adding two 3-digit numbers, and then progresses to using three or four numbers consisting of different numbers of digits that can be made using place value cards.

Plenary session

◆ *"What was the most important thing you have been learning?"* (Partitioning and using this to add numbers.) Give them some mental practice at adding multiples of 10 and 100. For example, *"What are 5 tens add 8 tens?"* or *"What are 3 hundreds add 8 hundreds? Can you write that on the board?"* Explain that for much of their work they have been adding long runs of small numbers or only two or three larger numbers. The method they were using today will help when they have several large numbers to add.

Further activities

◆ Play '4-in-a-row games' (see generic sheet 4 on page 93). The children use a square grid, such as 6 x 6, and fill in the numbers 1–36 randomly. They throw a dice three times to get three separate digits, which can be used with + or – to make one of the numbers on the board. For example, using 2, 4 and 5 it is possible to make 11, 1, 7, 21 and 29. A partner checks the calculation and if it is correct the number can be covered. The first to get four counters in a row (column or diagonal) is the winner.

Extension

◆ Use partitioning to develop understanding of decomposition.

Support

◆ Use 1–9 cards to make 2-digit numbers. Show how these are partitioned into tens and ones by putting straws into bundles of 10 and singles, strings of 10 beads or paper clips, and so on. Show this using place value cards.

26
©Hopscotch Educational Publishing

developing
Numeracy
Skills

Numeracy
Year 4/P5

✦ The Dinosaur Museum ✦

The **DINOSAUR** Museum

Admission charges
Adults   £2.50
Children £1.00

1. How much is it for 1 adult and 1 child?

2. How much is it for 2 adults and 2 children?

3. A class of 35 children and 4 adults went to the museum.
   How many people?

4. On Monday 16 children visited the museum.
   On Tuesday 21 children visited the museum.

   How many more children went on Tuesday?

5. From the museum shop, Mary bought:
   a rubber
   a pencil
   a toy dinosaur
   a packet of stickers

39p

Stickers

25p

10p

50p

   How much did she spend?

   She had £2. How much change did she get?

6. You buy 2 dinosaurs. Write their names
   and how much you pay altogether.

The **DINOSAUR** Museum

MODEL DINOSAUR PRICES
Brontosaurus   £2.50
Tyrannosaurus   £3.50
Stegosaurus   95p
Allosaurus   £1.25

_____

_____

 Pretend you have £5 to spend. Write what you could buy.

◆ The Dinosaur Museum ◆

For each of these questions, write how you found your answers.

1. On Thursday, 135 people visited the Dinosaur Museum. On Saturday there were 55 more visitors than on the Thursday.
   How many people visited the museum on Saturday?

2. Out of the 275 people who went to the museum on Friday, 125 were adults.
   How many children were there?

3. A group of school children visited the museum. There were 32 children in one class, 35 in another and 35 in the third class. There were 10 adults with them. How many people were there altogether?

4. A baby Brontosaurus measured 210cm when it was born. It had grown 282cm by its first birthday.
   How long was it when it was one year old?

5. The Stegosaurus in the museum was 245cm long. The Iguanodon measured 150cm more. Which dinosaur was longer?

   How long was it?

Pretend you have £10 to spend.
Write what you could buy.

£1.50   £2.75   £2.15   £3.50   £1.25

Photocopiable

developing **Numeracy Skills**

✦ The Dinosaur Museum ✦

For each of these questions, write how you found your answers.

1. The Dinosaur Museum had 375 visitors one week
    and 450 visitors the next week.

    How many visitors was this altogether?

2. How many more visitors came in the

    second week?

3. Some school children visited the museum. That day there
    were 124 more children than adults. If there were 256

    visitors altogether, how many were adults?

4. Admission costs £2.50 for an adult and £1.25 for a child.

    How much does it cost for 2 adults and 2 children?

    How much change will they have from £10?

5. The Tyrannosaurus in the museum was 1200cm long.
    The Iguanodon measured 910cm.

    Which was the longer dinosaur?

    How much longer was it?

6. In the museum shop, rubbers were packed in 5 layers and there were 20 in each
    each layer. 15 rubbers from a box had been sold. How many were left?

Pretend you have £10 to spend. Write what you
could buy and what change you get.

£1.50

£2.75

£2.15

£3.50

£1.25

developing
Numeracy
Skills

Addition and subtraction – 2

 Overall learning objectives

✦ Know and use addition and subtraction facts up to 20.
✦ Count up through multiples of 10, 100, and 1000.
✦ Count on and back in thousands, hundreds or tens.
✦ Add and subtract 9, 19, 29, for example by adding a multiple of 10 and adjusting.
✦ Use the vocabulary of addition and subtraction.
✦ Begin to understand the principles of commutative and associative laws.
✦ Add several small numbers.

LESSON ONE
HOW MANY?

 Assessment focus

Can the children add or subtract to the nearest multiple of 10 and adjust?

 Resources

✦ large and small 0–100 number lines
✦ 0–30 number lines
✦ dice marked 10, 20, 30, 10, 20 30 (or cards)
✦ dice marked +1 –1 +1 –1 +1 –1 (or cards)
✦ 0–90 dice and a +9 –9 +11 –11 +10 –10 dice/cards
✦ 0–9 cards
✦ wide strips of paper

 Oral work and mental calculation

Counting on or back

✦ Display a 0–100 number line. *"What must be added to 73 to make 80?"* Invite a child to show this on the number line. Then ask what must be added to 730 to make 800, or 7300 to make 8000. Continue by asking more addition and subtraction questions, where the answer can be found by counting across to the next 10s or 100s boundary. The children write their answers on

paper. Some might find it helpful to write the numbers in the questions as well.

 Starting point: whole class

✦ Display a number line. Give a 2-digit number and ask for suggestions about using the number line to add 9. Expect the children to add 10 and adjust by subtracting 1. Are there any other suggestions? Use another start number and ask how to add or subtract another near multiple of 10, such as 39 or 61. Demonstrate an example, such as 47 + 29.

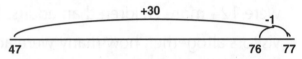

✦ Show how this method can be used to add 28, by adding 30 and adjusting by 2. Ask a volunteer to show this using the number line for 187–59. Expect them to do (187 – 60) + 1. Try a few more examples, encouraging mental calculation but with the option of using the number line.
✦ Write 100 on the board. Ask someone to throw a 10, 20, 30 dice and a +1, –1 dice. The answer is the score that is either added to or subtracted from the 100 on the board. This is continued as follows and becomes a long chain:

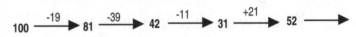

✦ The aim is to avoid getting to zero.

 Group activities

Focus group

Draw an addition square and discuss with the group how the missing numbers can be found using the number line. Complete a square together. Discuss strategies, such as when it is necessary to add and when to subtract. Give the group another square to complete in pairs, ensuring that both partners are fully involved.

+		11	
4	13		
		20	
10			39

developing
Numeracy Skills

Addition and subtraction – 2

The numbers and sizes of square can be adapted to the ability of the group.

+		19	
4	15		
		31	
10			39

+	31		28	101
				91
99		124		
11				
				150

As they are working assess their abilities to use inverse operations and the number line.

 Teacher-independent groups

Group 1: Working in pairs, this group continues the starter activity. Their start number is 30 and they use a number line and a set of cards marked +9 –9 +11 –11. As they do not have to make a decision about adding or subtracting numbers, the player who gets nearest to zero is the winner each time.

Group 2: This group also continues the starter activity, starting from the number 50 and using 10, 20, 30 and a +1, –1 dice. Some 0–100 number lines should be available.

Group 3: The start number for this group is 100. They throw the 0–90 and +9/–9/+11/–11/+10/–10 dice, the score on the latter being added to or subtracted from the former score. They might need to make informal jottings of number lines to aid their calculations.

✦ *Plenary session*

✦ *"Tell me how you have been adding and subtracting today."* (To the nearest multiple of 10 and adjusting.)

LESSON TWO
BE CAREFUL!

✦ Assessment focus

Can the children understand that although addition can be done in any order, this does not work for subtraction?

✦ Resources

✦ 0–9 cards

✦ Oral work and mental calculation

Mixed calculations

✦ Tell the children to work with a partner to draw a 6 x 6 grid and write in the numbers 1–36.

Demonstrate this on the board. Ask someone to turn over three cards and write them on the board. Ask the children if they can use the numbers to give an answer between 1 and 36. For example, if 2, 7 and 4 are turned over they could do 2 + 7 + 4 = 13, 27 + 4 = 31 or 2 x (7 + 4) = 22. Any calculations, with the answer, must be written on their paper and the answer crossed out on the 1–36 grid. The aim is to make as many answers as possible in five minutes. Share some of the calculations.

✦ Starting point: whole class

✦ Write two numbers on the board, for example 15 and 36. Ask a child to use the number line to add the two numbers, saying what they are doing. Are there different ways to find a solution? For example, was the larger number used first and the smaller one split into 10 and 5?

✦ Show how important it is to check that the sum of the numbers added or subtracted is correct. Next

Addition and subtraction – 2

ask someone to show how the difference between the numbers is found on the line, ensuring that they start from the larger number. Give another pair of numbers and ask for them to be added or subtracted in different ways. Get the children to draw what they do on an empty number line and leave these to help group 1. Work through some examples with larger numbers, such as 1435 and 233 and some calculations with missing numbers, like 234 + ☐ = 266, for groups 2 and 3.

 Group activities

 Focus group

Use this time to assess the children's understanding of associativity, or the fact that, for example: 25 + 26 + 19 can be written as (50 + 1) +19 or (19 + 1) +50. They then find the answers on a number line. Start by giving three 2-digit numbers and asking them for different ways of arranging the numbers to make adding easier. Write up their suggestions. Let them continue by making 2-digit numbers with 0–9 cards and finding different ways to add them. If they seem fairly confident, challenge them to add 2- and 3-digit numbers. Establish whether they understand that while rearranging numbers works for addition it does not work for subtraction.

 Teacher-independent groups

Activity sheet 1: This sheet requires the children to show different ways of adding and subtracting on a number line. The numbers are easily partitioned and they will need to use inverse operations to find missing numbers.

Activity sheet 2: This contains 2- and 3-digit numbers, bridging the nearest multiple of 10 or 100.

Activity sheet 3: This asks the children to find different ways to add and subtract the same numbers. Missing number calculations include 4-digit numbers.

 Plenary session

✦ Ask the focus group to demonstrate some of their numbers and ways of working, showing the order of addition does not matter. Ask children from the other groups to show how pairs of numbers were subtracted. Can they show that the order does matter for subtraction?

 Further activities

✦ Play '4-in-a-row' involving adding or subtracting numbers before or after multiples of 10, such as 156 + 49 or 284 – 38, which involve working to the nearest multiple of 10 and adjusting.

 Extension

✦ Write up the numbers 32, 63, 26, 15, 39 and 44, then this empty box calculation ☐ + ☐ = 70. The children have to choose from the numbers to complete the calculation. Do the same with ☐ – ☐ = 11.

 Support

✦ Play a simple version of '4-in-a-row', using interlocking cubes to help find the answers.

26	45	49	4	9
39	6	31	11	41
15	24	5	1	25
41	43	29	36	51
11	35	34	3	13

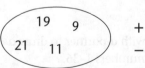

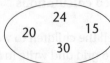

32
©Hopscotch Educational Publishing

developing
**Numeracy
Skills**

Numeracy
Year 4/P5

Name _____

◆ **Add and subtract** ◆

Show your answers on the number lines.

1.

Add 21 and 37 in 2 different ways.

_____

_____

2.

Add 27 and 45 in 2 different ways.

_____

_____

3.

Take 15 from 56 in 2 different ways.

_____

_____

4.

Find the difference between 83 and 25 in 2 different ways.

_____

_____

5.

Find the missing numbers. Show what you did.

a) $16 + \boxed{} = 25$ _____

b) $35 + \boxed{} = 72$ _____

c) $39 - \boxed{} = 26$ _____

 What must you subtract from

36, 49, 51, 82

to leave 15?

◆ Add and subtract ◆

Show your answers on the number lines.

1. Add 27 and 132 in 2 different ways.

_____

_____

2. Add 172 and 184 in 2 different ways.

_____

_____

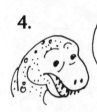

3. Subtract 36 from 150 in 2 different ways.

_____

_____

4. Find the difference between 145 and 372 in 2 different ways.

_____

_____

5. Find the missing numbers. Show what you did.

a) 145 + ⬜ = 270 _____

b) ⬜ + 57 = 260 _____

c) 148 − ⬜ = 90 _____

d) ⬜ − 120 = 250 _____

 Use the numbers 26, 15, 82 and 69 to make as many additions and subtractions as you can. Draw your answers on a number line.

✦ Add and subtract ✦

Show your answers on the number
lines.

1.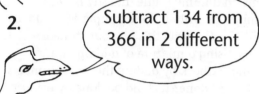

Add 134 and 366
in 2 different ways.

_____
_____

2.

Subtract 134 from
366 in 2 different
ways.

_____
_____
_____

3.

Add 286 and 591 in
2 different ways.

_____
_____

4.

Subtract 286 from
591 in 2 different
ways.

_____
_____

5.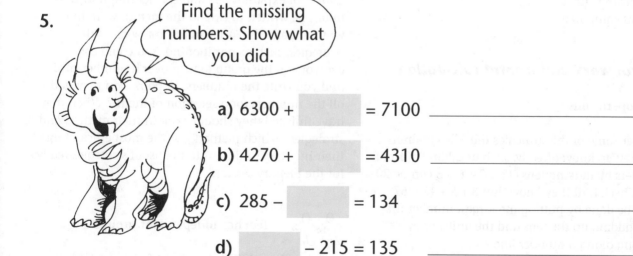

Find the missing
numbers. Show what
you did.

a) 6300 + ▢ = 7100 _____

b) 4270 + ▢ = 4310 _____

c) 285 − ▢ = 134 _____

d) ▢ − 215 = 135 _____

 Use the numbers 27, 314, 82 and 125 to make as many additions
and subtractions as you can. Draw your answers on a number line.

Using mental strategies

◆ Overall learning objectives

- ✦ Use knowledge of number facts and place value to add and subtract mentally.
- ✦ Use a variety of mental calculation strategies and talk about them using appropriate vocabulary.
- ✦ Explain methods and reasoning about numbers, orally and in writing.
- ✦ Develop written methods, building on mental strategies.

✦ LESSON ONE
HOW MANY?

◆ Assessment focus

Can the children explain their chosen method for a calculation and start to make jottings of their mental methods?

◆ Resources

- ✦ 100 squares
- ✦ number lines
- ✦ multiplication squares
- ✦ interlocking cubes
- ✦ base 10 equipment

◆ Oral work and mental calculation

Inverse operations

- ✦ Go over some of the strategies that the children are likely to know already, such as adding a list of numbers by making tens (13 + 7 + 6 + 3 can be 20 + 9). Check that they know that 3 + 5 + 12 + 67 could be done by putting the largest number first, or by adding up the tens and the units, or by hopping along a number line.
- ✦ Do some number line hopping with multiples of 10, for example 34 + 51.
- ✦ Draw a picture of the number line hops and the strategies used so far on the board. Display a list of the strategies.

◆ Starting point: whole class

- ✦ Display a 0–100 number line. Write a variety of calculations, such as 15 + □ + 10 = 30, 35 + 37, 74 + 300, 306 – 7, 5495 + 8 and 245 + 323.
- ✦ Discuss methods of solving these. For example, point to 15 + □ + 10 = 30 and ask someone to show this on a number line and say how the stages might be written, for example 15 + 10 = 25 and 30 – 25 = 5. (Write this on your strategies display as 'Using a mixture of adding and subtracting'.) Check by adding the three numbers.
- ✦ How is 35 + 37 done? It could be done by using near doubles. For 74 + 300 the suggestion may be to use a number line or just count on. 306 – 7 and 5495 + 8 can be solved by counting on or back, whereas for 245 + 323 it could be partitioning.
- ✦ Tell the groups that they will be doing similar calculations. For each one they will write what they did and explain their strategy. Leave the work on display.

◆ Group activities

        Focus group

Assess the children's range of strategies, encouraging clear oral explanations and considering how these might be written to extend the mental work into written methods. Focus on just a few mental strategies, such as partitioning. You could ask everyone in the group to turn over a number card and you write the numbers. In pairs, can they add all the numbers (or a selection of them)? When they have finished they should explain their method and strategies. Which method was the most efficient for their numbers? Add this to the list of strategies ready for the plenary session.

        Teacher-independent groups

Activity Sheet 1: This is a direct follow-on from the introduction of using near doubles, adding several small numbers, using addition and subtraction, and number lines. The children should use what they consider to be the appropriate strategy, then check

Using mental strategies

using another method and explain what they did using pictures and equipment.

Activity sheet 2: This is similar to Activity sheet 1 but the numbers are more demanding.

Activity sheet 3: Again, this is similar to the other activity sheets but with more challenging numbers.

◆ Plenary session

◆ Select some of the questions from the activity sheets and ask pairs of children to demonstrate

what they did. Read out (or write on the board) the explanation of what they did.

◆ Find out if other children from the groups worked the same way or differently. *"Which questions were the hardest to solve or explain? Why do you think this?"*

◆ Pose some similar questions but ask *"How would you do this?"* rather than just expecting them to give the answer. So you might say *"How will you add 260 and 270?"* or *"How will you subtract 76 from 100?"*

◆ Make the point that finding efficient methods will vary with the numbers and that there is no one 'right' way.

◆ LESSON TWO ◆
HOW WOULD YOU DO THIS?

◆ Assessment focus

Can the children select appropriate methods for a range of calculations?

◆ Resources

◆ number lines and squares for calculating
◆ 0–9 number cards

◆ Oral work and mental calculation

Addition to 100

◆ Organise the children into mixed ability groups of about four. Display a 100 square. Say *"Show me a pair of numbers that add to 100"* and let several children point out different pairs. Ask for three numbers with a sum of 100 and write up a few examples using their suggestions. Then tell the groups that they have five minutes to find as many ways as possible of making 100 using three

numbers. When time is up ask each team to give two examples and let the others check them. The teams count how many different ways they found.

◆ Starting point: whole class

◆ Write the number 50 on the board. Tell the children that you want to find as many ways of making 50 as possible. Allow a few minutes for pairs to write some calculations with an answer of 50. Invite each pair to tell everyone (or write on the board) their hardest calculation and say how they worked it out. Discuss which were facts they just knew, which ones they worked out and whether there are other facts they might work out using equipment, such as number lines, 100 squares, multiplication squares and cubes.

◆ Explain that each independent group will have a target number to write at the top of the page and their calculations will go in three lists: known facts, answers they work out and harder calculations needing the use of equipment. They can use any operation and, when adding, more than two numbers can be used. Ask them to try to write some calculations in each list and say that if number lines or squares are used they should write what was done.

Using mental strategies

◆ Group activities

Focus group

Draw a 6 x 6 grid and write in the numbers 1–36. Demonstrate this on the board. Ask someone to turn over three number cards and write the digits on the board. Say *"How can you use those digits in a calculation to make an answer between 1 and 36?"* So if 2, 7 and 4 are turned over they could do: 2 + 7 + 4 = 13, 27 + 4 = 31 or 2 x (7 + 4) =22, and so on. Show them how they could use other operations, like (7 x 4) ÷2. Write up any calculations with the answer.

Teacher-independent groups

Group 1: Give this group a target of 10 and make a variety of equipment available. They may need to start with addition and subtraction, but encourage them to use other operations by using equal jumps on the number line or equal sets for multiplication and division.

Group 2: This group should make 25. They can be asked to think about doubles and halves that might equal 25. Suggest they try to use all the operations.

Group 3: Working in pairs, these children can make a 2-digit target number using their 0–9 cards. They need to be challenged to use a greater range of strategies for making their target number. You might suggest they use brackets, if they have experienced them, and use different operations within a calculation.

◆ Plenary session

◆ Ask pairs from each group to explain which of their calculations they found most difficult and the reason for this. Which section of the paper was it written in?

◆ Further activities

◆ Extend the display from Lesson One and refer to this over the next few weeks as you give repeated practice in explaining a variety of mental methods.

◆ Extend rough jottings made and continue to ask children to explain them to the whole group. Partitioning is particularly well suited to developing written methods so give the children a complex calculation, such as 234 + 281 and gradually move towards quick written methods.

◆ Use the 'Finding a way' activity on generic sheet 3 (page 92).

◆ Extension

◆ These children can take the lead in linking mental methods to quicker written methods.

◆ Use the 'Finding a way' activity on generic sheet 3 (page 92), putting in numbers with a function, for example +, – or x in front of the numbers.

◆ Support

◆ Give these children more opportunity to work with one or two strategies practically, such as adding several small digits and grouping in tens.

◆ How did you do it? ◆

Write and draw what you did.

1. 3 + ▨ + 10 + 3 = 20

2. 16 + 18 = ▨

3. 2 + 4 + 8 + 1 + 6 = ▨

4. 19 + 36 = ▨

5. 5 + 3 + 2 + 26 = ▨

 Write some calculations you would do with near doubles.

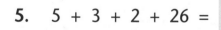

✦ How did you do it? ✦

Write about what you did.

1. 21 + ☐ + 38 = 100

2. 259 + 262 = ☐

3. 854 – ☐ = 454

4. 39 + 1236 = ☐

5. 29 + 14 + 11 + 5 + 16 = ☐

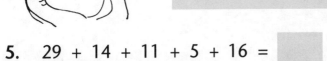

6. 360 + ☐ = 1000

 Write some calculations you could do on a number line.

developing
Numeracy Skills

✦ How did you do it? ✦

1. 630 + ▢ = 800

Write what you did after each answer.

_____

_____

2. 726 + 723 = ▢

_____

_____

3. 375 + ▢ + 295 = 1000

_____

_____

4. 5496 + 35 = ▢

_____

_____

5. 38 + 14 + 22 + 17 + 26 = ▢

_____

_____

6. 3715 − 57 = ▢

_____

_____

7. 467 − 199 = ▢

_____

_____

Using 3-digit numbers, write some calculations that you would need to do by partitioning into hundreds, tens and ones.

Chapter 7

Multiplication and division

 Overall learning objectives

✦ Understand multiplication as repeated addition.
✦ Use known facts to solve multiplication and division problems.
✦ Use doubling, halving, x10, x20, x15.
✦ Use partitioning and distributive law for multiplication.
✦ Use known number facts and place value to multiply and divide mentally.
✦ Develop written methods for multiplication.

LESSON ONE
DOUBLES AND HALVES

 Assessment focus

Can the children solve multiplication and division problems using known facts?

 Resources

✦ multiplication squares
✦ large and small 1–100 number lines
✦ interlocking cubes
✦ 0–9 cards and a 1–6 dice
✦ place value cards
✦ multiplication and division cards (see below)

 Oral work and mental calculation

Adding and subtracting near multiples of 10

✦ Prepare some cards on which are written +9, –9, +11, –11, +99, –99, +101 and –101. Write ten 3-digit numbers on the board. Point to one number and hold up the +11 card, asking for the children to show the answer with 0–9 cards. Hold up the +99 card, point to the same number and ask to see the answer. Discuss how to calculate this mentally, such as by adding 100 and subtracting 1. Continue pointing to numbers, holding up a card and encouraging answers to be shown quickly.

 Starting point: whole class

✦ Write 45 x 4 on the board and ask the children how to do it. They might say by doing 40 x 4 and 5 x 4 then adding the answers, or some children might suggest ways of using doubling. Can they show these methods? What will they do if they cannot work out 40 x 4? Show them how to double 10 and double the answer. Ask some questions involving doubling twice, showing this is the same as multiplying by 4 and go on to questions where division might be a strategy, for example *"What is 12 x 15?"*. This could be worked out as (12 x 10) + (12 x 5). Show them that if they cannot do 12 x 5, the answer to 12 x 10 can be halved. Suggest to the groups that they work in pairs and discuss how to solve their problems by doubling and halving.

✦ Show how tables can be built up using doubles. Write on the board the numbers that each of the independent groups will be multiplying by. Group 1 will be multiplying by 4, group 2 by 4 and 5 and group 3 by 16 and 15.

 Group activities

Focus group

Write the first five multiples of 2 , 4 and 8.

2	4	6	8	10
4	8	12	16	20
8	16	24	32	40

What can the children say about them? They should notice that the numbers are doubling downwards each time. Tell them they are going to use doubling for multiplying other numbers. Give them the calculation 25 x 8 and invite suggestions for working it out. Show how to write the doubling systematically:

25 x 1 = 25
25 x 2 = 50
25 x 4 = 100
25 x 8 = 200

Ask for predictions about continuing the doubling. Pose the question 45 x 8 (or 45 x 4 and so on, depending on the group's ability) and let them work it out, discussing their strategies for doubling

Multiplication and division

numbers. Try another problem together (involving multiplication by 16 for a more able group). Then ask how to solve 21 x 9. One method could be (21 x 8) + (21 x 1). Conclude by asking how they could solve 96 ÷ 8 (or 48 ÷ 4) and discussing strategies.

 Teacher-independent groups

Group 1: This group needs 1–9 and 10–30 place value cards to make a 2-digit number that is multiplied by 4 by doubling and doubling again. The numbers are partitioned, each part of the number is multiplied and the products added. They should repeat this with other numbers.

Group 2: In pairs the children should throw a 0–90 and a 1–6 dice. They add the scores and use doubling to multiply by 8 and halving to multiply by 5. They should explain how they worked.

 **LESSON TWO
USING KNOWN FACTS**

Assessment focus

Can the children explain and use the relationship between multiplication and division?

Oral work and mental calculation

Multiplication tables

✦ As a whole class, build up a multiplication square together.

x	2	3	4		10
2				10	
3					
	8				
	10				
10				50	100

Group 3: This group should make 2-digit numbers using 0–9 cards. For each number they use doubling to multiply by 16, doubling and halving to multiply by 15.

Plenary session

✦ Choose a pair of children from each group, including the focus group, to show on the board how they solved one of their problems. *"Did you all use the same or different methods?"* Write some single digit numbers on the board and ask how these might be multiplied by 25. Can they explain possible methods?

Starting point: whole class

✦ Give out multiplication squares to pairs of children. Remind them how these are used for multiplication and division. Set tasks using a range of vocabulary, such as *"Find the product of 6 and 7"* and *"What is 72 divided by 9?"*

✦ Give answers such as 20 and ask the class to find different ways of getting that answer, for example 4 x 5 = 20 and 2 x 10 = 20. Write these up as they are suggested. When about 10 examples have been given, discuss the different ways these could be said, such as 5 sets of 4, 4 multiplied by 5, the 5th multiple of 4 and so on.

✦ Ask *"Now can you write a division question with an answer of 20?"* Write some division problems to go with each of the multiplication statements where both have the same answer. Again emphasise the vocabulary of division, writing up some of the words in the questions.

Chapter 7

Multiplication and division

✦ Group activities

Focus group

Draw this grid on the board.

X		5	4
		32	
7	14		42
9			
	40		

or use a simpler version for less able children:

X	3		
2			10
	12		
		20	5

Can the children suggest a strategy for filling in the missing numbers? Discuss what operation is needed to solve the problems. Less able children might need to use multiplication squares or interlocking cubes. Help the group to establish the parts that are easy to work out, stressing that although it is a multiplication square they will have to use the inverse (division) to find answers. Complete the square together and give the children the following one to work out in pairs.

X		10	6
	27		
4	12		32
7			
	50		

Teacher-independent groups

Activity sheet 1: This sheet contains multiplication and division problems that have the same answer. Some questions are partly written in words to consolidate the appropriate vocabulary. There are some open-ended multiplication and division questions where the answer is given and children write the factors that make the answer.

Activity sheet 2: This is similar to Activity sheet 1, but with more difficult calculations.

Activity sheet 3: Again, this is similar to the other activity sheets, but contains more difficult calculations.

✦ Plenary session

✦ "What is the connection between multiplication and division?"
✦ "How are they the same and how are they different?"
✦ "What did you enjoy in maths today?"
✦ "What did you find difficult?"

Further activities

✦ Complete multiplication square jigsaw puzzles. (Multiplication squares cut along the lines to make about 8 pieces.)

Extension

✦ Balance different ways of making the number in the triangle.

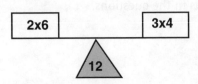

✦ Explore some simple factor 'trees'.

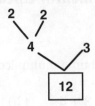

✦ Support

✦ Give support with counting equal sets, sharing and equal subtraction, using practical apparatus.

developing Numeracy Skills

✦ Match them up ✦

1. Join the dinosaurs that have the same answers.

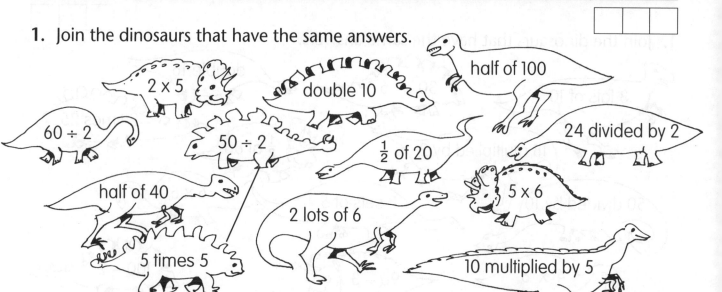

2. Fill in these boxes.

☐ x ☐ = 10   10 ÷ ☐ = ☐

- -

☐ x ☐ = 12   ☐ ÷ ☐ = 12

- -

☐ x ☐ = 12   ☐ ÷ ☐ = 12

- -

☐ x ☐ = 16   ☐ ÷ ☐ = 16

- -

☐ x ☐ = 16   ☐ ÷ ☐ = 16

Find lots of possible answers to this.   ☐ x ☐ = 24

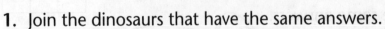

✦ **Match them up** ✦

1. Join the dinosaurs that have the same answers.

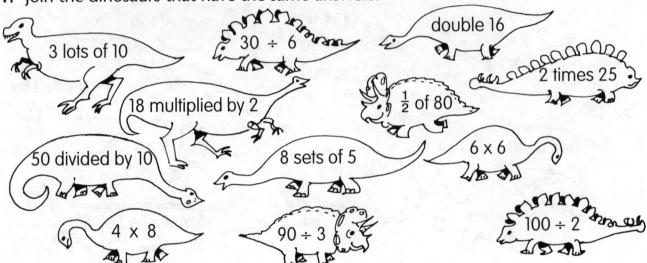

3 lots of 10

30 ÷ 6

double 16

18 multiplied by 2

$\frac{1}{2}$ of 80

2 times 25

50 divided by 10

8 sets of 5

6 × 6

4 × 8

90 ÷ 3

100 ÷ 2

2. Fill in these boxes.

☐ × ☐ = 20   ☐ ÷ ☐ = 20

☐ × ☐ = 10   ☐ ÷ ☐ = 10

☐ × ☐ = 24   ☐ ÷ ☐ = 24

☐ × ☐ = 100   100 ÷ ☐ = ☐

☐ × ☐ = 96   ☐ ÷ ☐ = 96

Find lots of possible answers to this.   ☐ × ☐ = 48

developing **Numeracy Skills**

✦ Match them up ✦

1. Join the dinosaurs that have the same answers.

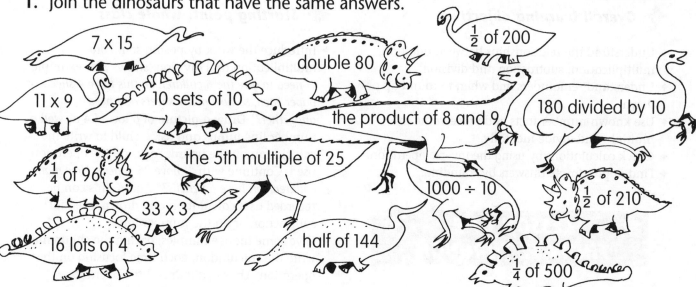

- 7 × 15
- 11 × 9
- 10 sets of 10
- double 80
- $\frac{1}{2}$ of 200
- the product of 8 and 9
- 180 divided by 10
- $\frac{1}{4}$ of 96
- the 5th multiple of 25
- 33 × 3
- 1000 ÷ 10
- $\frac{1}{2}$ of 210
- 16 lots of 4
- half of 144
- $\frac{1}{4}$ of 500

2. Fill in these boxes.

$\boxed{} \times \boxed{} = 36$ $\boxed{} \div \boxed{} = 36$

$\boxed{} \times \boxed{} = 36$ $\boxed{} \div \boxed{} = 36$

$\boxed{} \times \boxed{} = 32$ $\boxed{} \div \boxed{} = 32$

$\boxed{} \times \boxed{} = 50$ $\boxed{} \div \boxed{} = 50$

$\boxed{} \times \boxed{} = 100$ $\boxed{} \div \boxed{} = 100$

 Find lots of possible answers to this. $\boxed{} \times \boxed{} = 96$

Solving number problems

Overall learning objectives

◆ Understand the relationships between addition, multiplication, subtraction and division.
◆ Understand remainders and when to round up or down.
◆ Use known number facts and place value to multiply and divide mentally.
◆ Check calculations by using the inverse operation.
◆ Find approximate answers by rounding.

**LESSON ONE
THINK IT THROUGH**

Assessment focus

Can the children use multiplication and division to solve problems using a range of vocabulary?

Resources

◆ 0–100 number line
◆ multiplication squares
◆ number lines
◆ interlocking cubes

Oral work and mental calculation

Number sequences

◆ Display a 0–100 number line. Write a sequence of numbers, such as 23, 25, 27, 29. Ask the children to tell you the next three numbers in the series. Repeat this with other patterns: 2, 5, 8, 11; some with different sized steps: 0, 1, 3, 4, 6, 7; some that count back or use multiplication.
◆ Working in groups of four, ask the children to devise a sequence. Then let the groups in turn write the first few numbers in their sequence and the others predict the next three terms.
◆ Point to the first number in some sequences and ask, *"What number might go before this one?"*

Starting point: whole class

◆ Introduce the work by posing some oral multiplication and division 'stories', for example *"I need to give the 6 children on this table 4 sheets of paper each, so how many sheets do I need altogether?"* Draw a picture of 6 lots of 4 as well as number line jumps and ask a child to write the calculation on the board. Focus on the operation used. Continue with *"I have 25 pencils. How many children can have 6 pencils?"* Again, this can be recorded as a calculation and drawn as equal subtraction or on the number line.
◆ Give some more examples, asking the children to write the calculation, each time focusing on the operation. They could draw little operation dinosaurs as on the activity sheets.
◆ Prompt thinking about whether answers will be larger, or smaller, than the starting numbers, because this will indicate the operation needed (see the oral work in Lesson Two).
◆ Explain the group work about visiting the Dinosaur Museum. Say that they must write the calculation and operation each time as well as the answer.

Group activities

Focus group

Say *"A class of 30 children are going to visit the Dinosaur Museum. Together we will write x and ÷ number stories."* Talk about the factors of 30, using apparatus if necessary, and ask the children to write as many multiplication and division number sentences as they can with the factors (2, 15, 3, 10, 5 and 6). Take one number sentence and discuss the sort of story that could be told. For example 30 ÷ 3 = 10 could be *"On the bus the 30 children sit 3 to a seat, so 10 seats are needed"*. Assess the vocabulary of multiplication and division in the context of word problems and whether they can write story problems that reflect a number sentence. Extend the activity by posing some questions with remainders, such as *"If only 4 children can touch the dinosaur footprint at a time, how many groups will there be?"* Discuss whether the number needs rounding up or down.

developing **Numeracy Skills**

Solving number problems

 Teacher-independent groups

Activity sheet 1: The 'story' problems on this sheet can be solved through equal addition or subtraction. Some children may need the support of practical apparatus or number lines. The main aim is for decisions to be made about the operation to be used for each question.

Activity sheet 2: The problems on this sheet are similar to those on Activity sheet 1 but the mathematics is more demanding.

Activity sheet 3: Again, the problems on this sheet are similar to those on the other activity sheets but the mathematics is more demanding.

LESSON TWO IS IT RIGHT?

◆ Assessment focus

Can the children check their work using different strategies?

◆ Resources

✦ 1–20 and 1–6 dice.
✦ 0–9 cards

◆ Oral work and mental calculation

Solving empty box problems

✦ Write up some calculations with missing numbers, such as $\triangle + \triangle = 25$, $\triangle - \triangle = 25$, $\triangle \times \triangle = 25$ and $\triangle \div \triangle = 25$.
✦ The children work in pairs to find as many answers as possible. Give them a few minutes and ask for some solutions to be written on the board. They should observe that there are only 3 solutions to $\triangle \times \triangle = 25$ (5 x 5, 25 x 1 and 1 x 25), whereas $\triangle - \triangle = 25$ has an unlimited number.

◆ Plenary session

✦ Two or three children from each group can read one of their questions and explain to the class how they solved it. Discuss whether other children used different methods and if the answers were the same.
✦ *"What have you learned today about solving story problems?"*
✦ *"Tell me something you know about multiplication."* It makes numbers bigger (unless you multiply by 1 or a number less than 1).

✦ Give calculations where the operation is missing: $36 \triangle 2 = 72$, $81 \triangle 9 = 9$, $35 \triangle 59 = 94$ and $80 \triangle 26 = 54$.
✦ Give them time to discuss these and ask for the solutions. How did they solve the problems? Discuss the fact that with addition or multiplication answers are higher than either number, whereas with subtraction or division the answer will be lower than the first number.

◆ Starting point: whole class

✦ Give the calculation 19 x 8. Discuss how the answer can be found. Suggestions might include (20 x 8) –8 or (10 x 8) + (9 x 8) or 29 doubled three times. Show how partitioning could be used, (10 x 9) + (9 x 8). Try all the suggestions to see if all the answers are the same. Ask if there are any other ways of checking whether answers are correct. Demonstrate using the inverse (division) for checking. Ask one person to turn over two number cards and make a 2-digit number and another child to throw a 1–6 dice. Write the numbers as a multiplication, such as 45 x 2. Try different ways together of getting the answer and recording them. Show the groups how to generate the numbers they will work with.

Numeracy
Year 4/P5

developing
Numeracy
Skills

©Hopscotch Educational Publishing

49

Solving number problems

◆ Group activities

Focus group

Ask the group to give you four different single-digit numbers, such as 2, 4, 5 and 6. (A less able group could use 1, 2 and 4.) Ask them to multiply all the numbers together in any order, doing one example together. Check everyone has the same answer. *"Which order was easiest?"* Discuss checking with division. Assess their understanding that multiplication can be done in any order but division cannot. Repeat this with another set of numbers and again get the children to check answers in different ways. If they are fairly confident include some 2-digit numbers.

Teacher-independent groups

Group 1: These children should turn over a card from the 1–9 set and throw a 1–20 dice to get their two numbers. They find the product and then try two other methods to check the answer. Ask the group to record what they do each time.

Group 2: This group makes a 2- digit number with cards and throws a 1–6 dice for their two numbers. They should work in the same way as group 1 and prepare to share their methods during the plenary session.

Group 3: Let this group make 2-digit numbers with 0–9 cards and throw a 0–9 dice for the number to multiply by. Tell them they need to check their answers in at least three different ways and to record what they have done each time to share later.

Plenary session

✦ Invite representatives from each group to show how they found the product with their first pair of numbers and how they checked the answers. The focus group can explain how they used the inverse to check multiplication of several digits.
✦ *"Why is checking important?"*
✦ *"What did you learn today about the word 'inverse'?"*

Further activities

✦ Using a set of four numbers, the children can explore how many products can be made. They should check their calculations using different methods.
✦ Ask the children to look at home to find situations where multiplication and division are used. For example, 3 apples are needed every day for school lunch boxes. How many are needed to last the week?
✦ Use the 'Finding a way' activity on generic sheet 3 (page 92). You could white out some numbers and put in some that add to 100. The children have to find their way out by adding exactly to 100.

Extension

✦ Using a 6 x 6 square the children investigate the factors of all the numbers.
✦ Use the 'Dinosaur footprint' activity on generic sheet 5 (page 94). Write in numbers where the children have to decide how to make the next number. For example, to get from 13 to 16 they add 3. They should write what they did on the sheet. Do different sheets for different abilities.

Support

✦ Give a set of numbers up to 20 and find which ones can be made into rectangular arrays.

✦ Think it out ✦

Fill in one or more of these for each calculation below that you do.

1.a) At the museum these children work in 2s. Draw the 2s.

How many 2s? ▨

b) Adults look after groups of 4.

How many 4s? ▨

2. Stickers are 50p ⊙ a pack and there are 5 in a pack.

Darren buys 3 packs.

a) How many stickers altogether? ▨

b) How much does he pay? ▨

3. 6 children buy 4 dinosaur pencils each.

How many pencils do they have altogether? ▨

Write x and ÷ stories using 2, 5 and 10 about the Dinosaur Museum.

developing Numeracy Skills

✦ Think it out ✦

Write and draw what you do each time.
Fill in one or more operation dinosaurs to
show the operation you used.

1. A class of 36 children goes to the Dinosaur Museum by minibus.
    The same number go on each minibus. A minibus carries 12 people.

    How many minibuses were needed?

    What I did:

2. The children found that Tyrannosaurus has 3 toes on each back foot.

    How many toes does it have altogether?

    How many toes did a group of 6 Tyrannosaurus have?

    What I did:

3. The museum shop sells dinosaur stickers. There are 8 stickers in one pack.

    Lucy wants 24 stickers. How many packs does she buy?

    Darren wants 40 stickers. How many packs does he buy?

    What I did:

4. Ben buys 3 dinosaur pencils for each of his 3 friends.

    How many pencils does he buy?

    1 pencil costs 49p. How much does he pay?

    What I did:

　　Write some multiplication and division stories about
　　　　36 children visiting the Dinosaur Museum shop.

developing
**Numeracy
Skills**

✦ Think it out ✦

Write how you find the answers.
Show the operation you used.

1. A party of 72 schoolchildren went to the Dinosaur Museum.

   a) It cost £1.50 admission for each child.

   How much was this altogether?

   What I did:

   b) A quarter of the 72 children worked in the Tyrannosaurus room.

   How many children were in the room?

   What I did:

2. The children found that Brachiosaurus weighed about 84 tonnes.
   This is 12 times more than an African elephant.

   How much does the elephant weigh?

   What I did:

3. There were 9 dinosaur stickers in each pack. Ranjit wanted 50 stickers.

   How many packs did he have to buy?

   Did he get exactly the right number?

   What I did:

 Write some multiplication and division stories about the children
visiting the Dinosaur Museum shop. Give them to your friend to try.

Fractions

 Overall learning objectives

+ Use fraction notation and recognise some equivalent fractions.
+ Find fractions of numbers or quantities.
+ Recognise the equivalence between fractions and decimals.
+ Solve 'real life' problems involving fractions.
+ Understand that division is used to find fractions of numbers.

LESSON ONE
ARE THEY EQUAL?

 Assessment focus

Can the children recognise and use equivalent fractions?

 Resources

+ sorting toys and interlocking cubes
+ fraction sets, showing equivalence
+ number lines
+ paper strips
+ coloured paper
+ a dice marked $\frac{1}{2}$, $\frac{1}{4}$, $\frac{1}{8}$, $\frac{1}{8}$, $\frac{1}{16}$ and $\frac{1}{16}$.

 Oral work and mental calculation

Mental multiplication strategies

+ Say, *"I need the answer to 38 x 5. How shall I do it?"* Give the children time for discussion in pairs about some strategies. Suggestions might include, *"You do 40 x 5 and take away 2 x 5"* or *"You multiply by 10 and halve the answer"* and so on. Discuss the children's methods.
+ Write up some other numbers to multiply by 5 and tell them to try at least two different methods to check that the answers are the same. Share their methods and decide on the most effective. *"Can the same strategy be used to solve 27 x 50 and, if so, how?"*

 Starting point: whole class

+ Show a strip of paper and ask someone to find half. This will probably be done by folding. How many halves are there? Ask for quarters and find them by folding. Continue to 16ths.
+ Write $1 = \frac{2}{2} = \frac{4}{4} = \frac{8}{8} = \frac{16}{16}$. Can the children predict what comes next in the sequence? Say *"These are equivalent fractions because they are different ways of writing the same thing. Today you will be working with different fractions to find ones that are equivalent."*
+ Tell the groups which fractions they will work with and show group 1 how to start with fractions equivalent to a half.

 Group activities

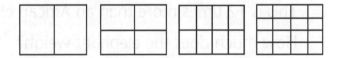 Focus group

Provide different colours of A4 paper for the children to fold into halves, quarters, eighths and sixteenths (use a different colour for each).

Ask questions such as *"How many sixteenths will fit on top of a quarter?"* Discuss equivalent fractions, for example $\frac{4}{16} = \frac{1}{4}$, and write them on a large sheet of paper. Each pair takes some of each fraction pieces (cut out from the coloured paper), a piece of A4 card for a playing board and the $\frac{1}{2}$, $\frac{1}{4}$, $\frac{1}{8}$, $\frac{1}{8}$, $\frac{1}{16}$ and $\frac{1}{16}$ dice. In turn, each player throws the dice, selects the fraction shown and places it on their board. If a fraction is thrown and there is not space on the board for it, that turn is missed. As the children are playing ask questions relating to equivalent fractions like *"You have put on four sixteenths. What other fraction is the same?"* and *"How many eighths have you scored? how would you write that?"* For a less able group use only halves, quarters and eighths.

Fractions

 Teacher-independent groups

Group 1: By folding strips of paper this group uses halves, quarters and eighths to find fractions equivalent to a half, a quarter and three-quarters. For example, they use:

$\frac{1}{2}$		$\frac{1}{2}$	
$\frac{1}{4}$	$\frac{1}{4}$	$\frac{1}{4}$	$\frac{1}{4}$
$\frac{1}{8}$ $\frac{1}{8}$ $\frac{1}{8}$ $\frac{1}{8}$ $\frac{1}{8}$ $\frac{1}{8}$ $\frac{1}{8}$ $\frac{1}{8}$			

To find:

$\frac{1}{2}$	
$\frac{1}{4}$	$\frac{1}{4}$
$\frac{1}{8}$ $\frac{1}{8}$ $\frac{1}{8}$ $\frac{1}{8}$	

Encourage them to use prediction about sixteenths by looking at patterns.

Group 2: This group divides 18cm long strips of paper to make thirds, sixths and ninths by measuring. They find the number of each fraction equivalent to a whole, a third, two thirds, a sixth, two sixths and so on and record systematically to find patterns and predict how they develop.

Group 3: This group uses 20cm strips of paper to make fifths, tenths and twentieths. They start by finding equivalents of one fifth, two fifths and so on.

◆ *Plenary session*

◆ *"What have you learned about equivalent fractions?"* Ask a pair from each group to show their equivalent fraction patterns. *"How do you think the patterns continue?"*

◆ Write up $\frac{1}{3} = \frac{2}{6} = \frac{}{8}$ and so on. Write up some other fractions, like $\frac{25}{100}$ and ask the children to think of an equivalent fraction, giving their reasons. Talk about ways of simplifying fractions.

◆ *"Which is greater, $\frac{1}{3}$ or $\frac{3}{8}$? Show me on your fraction strips how you know the answer."*

◆ LESSON TWO
LINKS WITH DIVISION

◆ *Assessment focus*

Can the children explain that division is used to find fractions of numbers?

◆ *Resources*

✦ toys for counting

Oral work and mental calculation

Find the sum and difference using 4 digits

✦ Can the children explain 'sum' and 'difference'? Write the following on the board.

| 2 | 5 | 3 | 8 |

✦ Ask them to find the sum of the numbers. How could they use the numbers to make a larger sum? Show how digits can be combined, for example 23 and 58. Can they find the sum of the new numbers? Can they find the difference between the totals? Give them time to complete three or four calculations, then ask if anyone has made a sum greater than 100. Discuss and put in order all the sums that were made. Which was the lowest sum anyone found? What was the smallest/largest difference and what methods were used?

◆ *Starting point: whole class*

✦ Count out 32 sorting toys together. Ask the children how to find half of the set. Show the set divided into two equal groups and ask how this is the same as halving numbers. Write $\frac{1}{2}$ of 32 = 16. Put the halves together and ask how to find a quarter of the toys. The children may suggest halving and halving again, or dividing by 4, so

Fractions

ask them to do this mentally and write the answer. Check by making four equal groups and counting them. Write the new fraction. Give other numbers and ask for a half and a quarter by working practically. This will help group 1 later. Now count out 30 toys and ask for suggestions about finding a tenth. If they seem unsure, count the toys into 10 equal sets and find how many in a set.

◆ Group activities

Focus group

Write up some fractions, such as $\frac{1}{2}$, $\frac{1}{4}$, $\frac{1}{10}$ and $\frac{1}{5}$ on a large sheet of paper. Ask why they are written as they are. Replies may include that half means one out of two pieces. Explain that it also means $1 \div 2$ and that to find half a number they divide by 2. Write some multiples of 2 and ask the children to halve them. Discuss any methods used. Give them some odd numbers to halve and show them how to write the remainders as a fraction, for example $\frac{1}{2}$ of 35 is $17\frac{1}{2}$. Continue doing this with quarters, starting with multiples of 4 and, if the group is confident, ask for a quarter of 17. *"What fraction is the remainder this time?"* They could then make some 2-digit numbers with 0–9 cards and divide them into quarters, writing the remainders as fractions. Extend this to finding tenths, with fractional remainders.

Teacher-independent groups

Activity Sheet 1: The children are asked to give an explanation about finding a half or a quarter of a number. Encourage them to discuss practical sorting into sets, and suggest they think about what they might do for division. This will help them to rehearse their contribution to the plenary session.

Activity Sheet 2: The main emphasis on this sheet is on finding quarters and tenths; the activity leads from pictorial grouping to working mentally or with the support of apparatus.

Activity Sheet 3: On this sheet a problem needs solving that involves the number of different types of dinosaur based on fractions of 20, including $\frac{3}{10}$. This is extended to fractions of 24.

◆ Plenary session

- ◆ Ask someone from group 3 to read their fraction problem to the class and explain their solution. Others in the group can explain what they did. Groups 1 and 2 had a simpler version of the problem, so ask them to share their solutions.
- ◆ Pose a similar problem. *"A farmer had 36 animals; a quarter were hens, a third pigs, a ninth cats and the rest were cows."* Stress that to find fractions of numbers we use division.

◆ Further activities

- ◆ Groups can make posters showing equivalent fractions. They fold and cut gummed paper, writing the equivalent fractions:

1 whole   2 halves   2 halves   4 quarters

- ◆ Give the problem *"If I have 3 pizzas, how can I share them between my 4 children?"* Use other numbers of pizzas and children.

◆ Extension

- ◆ Starting with a square of card, draw a seven-piece tangram puzzle (using the example to copy) ask the children to calculate the fraction each piece is of the whole puzzle.

◆ Support

- ◆ Make a set of 'weights' by halving, quartering and so on using a 200g piece of Plasticene. Talk about the fraction each 'weight' is of the 200g.

✦ Divide them up ✦

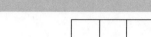

1. Put the same number of dinosaur eggs in each bag.

a) How many eggs altogether? ☐

b) How many in each set? ☐

c) What is half of 12? ☐

2. Put these eggs into four equal sets.

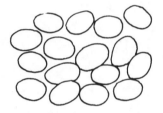 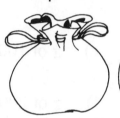 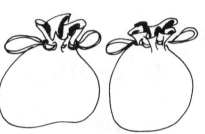 

a) How many eggs altogether? ☐

b) How many in each set? ☐

c) $\frac{1}{4}$ of ☐ = ☐

3. What is:

a) $\frac{1}{2}$ of 30? ☐   **b)** $\frac{1}{2}$ of 24? ☐   **c)** $\frac{1}{2}$ of 42? ☐

How did you find $\frac{1}{2}$ of a number? _____

4. What is:

a) $\frac{1}{4}$ of 20? ☐   **b)** $\frac{1}{4}$ of 24? ☐   **c)** $\frac{1}{4}$ of 36? ☐

How did you work them out? _____

_____

 There are 16 dinosaurs in one room of the museum. $\frac{1}{2}$ are Tyrannosaurus and $\frac{1}{4}$ are Stegosaurus. How many of each are there?

✦ Divide them up ✦

1.a) Show how you would find $\frac{1}{4}$ of these dinosaur eggs.

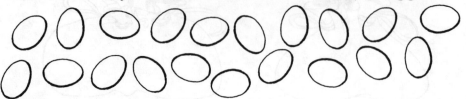 

b) There are [   ] eggs altogether.   **c)** $\frac{1}{4}$ of [   ] = [   ]

Explain what you did. _____

2. Finding $\frac{1}{4}$. What is:

a) $\frac{1}{4}$ of 24 [   ]   **b)** $\frac{1}{4}$ of 32 [   ]   **c)** $\frac{1}{4}$ of 100 [   ]

d) $\frac{1}{4}$ of 60 [   ]   **e)** $\frac{1}{4}$ of 48 [   ]   **f)** $\frac{1}{4}$ of 200 [   ]

3.a) Show how to find $\frac{1}{10}$ of these dinosaur eggs.

b) There are [   ] eggs altogether.   **c)** $\frac{1}{10}$ of [   ] = [   ]

d) Draw and write how you would find $\frac{1}{10}$ of 30.

4. Find $\frac{1}{10}$ of these numbers.

a) $\frac{1}{10}$ of 80 = [   ]   **b)** $\frac{1}{10}$ of 200 = [   ]

 In one room of the Dinosaur Museum are 20 dinosaurs. $\frac{1}{10}$ are Brontosaurus. $\frac{1}{5}$ are Diplodocus. How many are there of each?

✦ Divide them up ✦

1. Find a half. What is:

a) $\frac{1}{2}$ of 10 ___   **b)** $\frac{1}{2}$ of 30 ___   **c)** $\frac{1}{2}$ of 48 ___   **d)** $\frac{1}{2}$ of 84 ___

Explain how you found a half. _____

_____

2. Find a quarter. What is:

a) $\frac{1}{4}$ of 16 ___   **b)** $\frac{1}{4}$ of 44 ___   **c)** $\frac{1}{4}$ of 100 ___   **d)** $\frac{1}{4}$ of 160 ___

Explain how you found a quarter. _____

_____

3. What is:

a) $\frac{1}{10}$ of 50 ___   **b)** $\frac{1}{10}$ of 90 ___   **c)** $\frac{1}{10}$ of 100 ___

d) $\frac{1}{10}$ of 600 ___   **e)** $\frac{1}{10}$ of 750 ___   **f)** $\frac{1}{10}$ of 1500 ___

4.a) What fraction of £2 is 50p? ___   **b)** What fraction of £5 is 50p? ___

c) What fraction of 100p is 25p? ___

5. In the Dinosaur Museum there are 20 models. How many of each sort are there?

$\frac{1}{10}$ are Stegosaurus ___ $\frac{3}{10}$ are Brontosaurus ___

$\frac{1}{4}$ are Tyrannosaurus ___ $\frac{1}{5}$ are Diplodocus ___

 Write another fraction story for 24 dinosaurs.
Give it to your friend to try.

Decimals

◆ Overall learning objectives

◆ Develop an understanding that dividing 1 by 10 gives a decimal number.
◆ Understand the equivalence between fractions and decimals.
◆ Understand the value of a digit in decimal fractions.
◆ Order decimals on a number line.

LESSON ONE
ARE THEY THE SAME?

◆ Assessment focus

Can the children identify and use equivalent decimals and fractions?

◆ Resources

◆ straws
◆ 0–9 number cards
◆ small bags (not see-through)
◆ coloured cubes
◆ blank cards (playing card size)
◆ blank number lines

◆ Oral work and mental calculation

Factors and multiples

◆ Show the children some straws. Say that you are going to ask questions about the straws and they should show you the answer using their 0–9 cards.
◆ *"Imagine you have 12 straws. Use them to make separate squares. How many squares are there?"*
◆ *"With the same number of straws, how many triangles can you make? How many hexagons?"*
◆ Do the same with other quantities of straws.
◆ Try questions involving skeletal 3-D shapes.
◆ *"How many straws would you need to make the sides of a cube?"*
◆ *"If you had 48 straws how many skeleton cubes could you make?"*

◆ Starting point: whole class

◆ Draw a 0–1 number line divided into tenths.

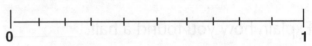

0   1

◆ *"Count the divisions. What fraction are they?"*
◆ Ask someone to write tenths above the line. Count in tenths together. Ask *"Is there another way to write the fractions?"* Remind them about writing a tenth of a pound as £0.10, or as it appears on a calculator. Together write the decimals under the line and count from 0–1 in 0.1s.
◆ Draw a line from 1–2 and write in the decimals. Count from 0–2 in tenths and decimals. How does this continue? Leave the 0–2 line on the board for group 1 to see. Give them a decimal between 0 and 2 and ask for the fraction, or vice versa.
◆ Extend this with numbers to 10, for example *"What is the same as 5.3?"*

◆ Group activities

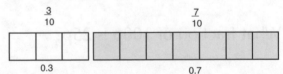 **Focus group**

Take 10 cubes in two different colours at random. Match the colours and ask how many tenths there are in each colour. *"What is that as a decimal?"* If you have 3 of one and 7 of another, show that 3 tenths and 7 tenths equals 1 and how these are written.

$\frac{3}{10}$ $\frac{7}{10}$

0.3   0.7

Give each pair of children a small bag. They put in a number of interlocking cubes of two colours. Both take 10 and record as decimals and fractions. If they seem confident they can continue by taking 20.

 Teacher-independent groups

Group 1: In pairs this group should make 0–2 number lines with tenths and decimals. One of the pair chooses a decimal number and writes it on a piece of card. Their partner writes the equivalent fraction on another card. They make five pairs of

Decimals

cards, then two pairs of children join making groups of four. Their 20 cards are placed face down on the table. The children play pelmanism by turning over two cards and if the numbers are equivalent that player keeps both. The player with most pairs wins.

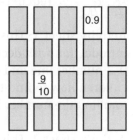

Group 2: This group should do the same as group 1, except they make a 0–5 number line and use decimal/fraction equivalents between those numbers to play pelmanism.

LESSON TWO
WHERE DOES IT GO?

◆ Assessment focus

Can the children work with decimal fractions and put them in order?

◆ Resources

✦ 0–100 number line
✦ open-topped abacus with beads

◆ Oral work and mental calculation

Number line counting

✦ Practise counting in 2s, 3s and so on from different starting points. Display a 0–100 number line. Give the starting and ending numbers:
✦ *"Start at 1 and count in twos up to 29."*
✦ *"Start at 52 and count in twos up to 100."*
✦ *"Start at 59 and count back in threes to 20."*
✦ Talk about the patterns and which were the easiest to count. Give some higher starting numbers, for example *"Count in hundreds from 101 to 1001"*, and so on.

Group 3: This group works with decimals and fractions between 0 and 10 (although an able group could go beyond this).

◆ Plenary session

✦ Write some fractions and decimals on the board. Ask the children to write the equivalent underneath each saying why they think that is correct. Finish by asking for the equivalents of higher numbers, such as 129.4.
✦ *"What have you learned today about fractions and decimals?"*

◆ Starting point: whole class

✦ Draw a long 0–5 number line. Tell the children that they will be looking at what goes in between the numbers. Mark divisions showing tenths. Count them together. Ask what fraction each division is. Show how the divisions between 0 and 1 can be written as $\frac{1}{10}$ or 0.1. Ask *"Where will 0.9 go on the line? Can someone write where it goes?"* Give other decimals for them to position. *"Why did you put it there? Which part of the number helps you decide the size?"* Show that whole numbers should be written as 1.0 and so on.
✦ Write three or four decimal numbers. Ask *"Which is the largest/smallest?"* Ask them to order the numbers and give their reasons. Say some fractions for them to write. *"Write 1 as a decimal."* or *"How do you write $2\frac{3}{10}$?"* Leave these on the board to help group 1.

◆ Group activities

 Focus group

On a large sheet of paper draw a 0–0.1 number line. Draw intervals showing hundredths and ask the children what these might be worth. Show how this is written as 0.01. Remind them of the effect of

Decimals

dividing by 10 (the digits move one place to the right). Demonstrate this on a chart or abacus, with a decimal point marked.

Tens	Ones	•	Tenths	Hundredths
1	0	•	0	0
	1	•	0	0
	0	•	1	0
	0	•	0	1

Say some numbers, asking where these go on the line, such as *"Where would you put 0.05?"* Extend the line to 0.5. Point to different places and ask individuals to write in the hundredths. Make the link with how we write amounts of money. Write a 3-digit number. Demonstrate dividing by 10 and 10 again on a place value chart. Try another number and ask which is higher/lower. How do they decide? Say *"In pairs, make four 3-digit numbers, divide them by 10 and 10 again. Put your numbers in order from smallest to largest."* As the children work assess how they determine the order of the decimal numbers.

 Teacher-independent groups

Activity sheet 1: This sheet continues from the introduction with decimal numbers to write along a 0–2 number line and others to order. Show the children how to find three decimal numbers totalling the number line on the page.

Activity sheet 2: This sheet also includes conversion of pence into pounds. The three decimal numbers to be added make a total of 3. The number line on the sheet can be used to help.

Activity sheet 3: The ordering of decimals includes money, written both in pounds and in pence. This group finds the sum of four decimals equal to 10.

 Plenary session

✦ Ask children from each group to write up an example of a corner number problem and explain how they found the answer.

 Further activities

✦ Use a calculator to explore decimal remainders when whole numbers are divided by 4. Write the answers on a number line.
✦ Play the Dinosaur Footprint game (generic sheet 5 on page 94).

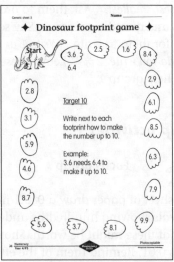

 Extension

✦ Play the decimal version of the '4-in-a-row' game (generic sheet 4 on page 93).

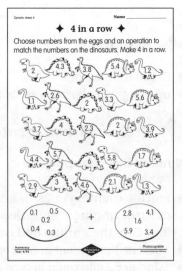

Support

✦ Groups of four children each take five coins and write the total as a decimal on card. The amounts are ordered from smallest to largest.

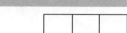

✦ Where do they go? ✦

1. Write the numbers on the line.

0   1   2

2. Where do these go? | 1.9 | | 1.1 | | 0.3 | | 0.8 | | 1.5 |

0   1   2

3. Put these numbers in order.

a)   2.3   5.1   0.2   1.4

   smallest   largest

b)   4.1   2.8   0.5   3.6

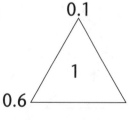   largest   smallest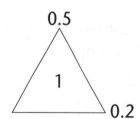

4. Write these as decimals.

a) one tenth   **b)** one and two tenths   **c)** five and a tenth

5. Make the corners add up to the middle number.

                   0.1   0.5

                      1   1

         0.6   0.2

    Draw more triangles. Write numbers on the corners that add up to 1.

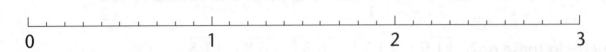

✦ **Where do they go?** ✦

1. Write where these numbers go on the number line.

| 2.6 | 0.1 | 1.5 | 2.1 | 1.9 | 0.9 |

```
├──┬──┬──┬──┬──┬──┬──┬──┬──┬──┬──┬──┬──┬──┬──┤
0              1              2              3
```

2. Put these numbers in order.

a)   4.7   3.4   6.5   0.3   5.8

[ ]   [ ]   [ ]   [ ]   [ ]

smallest   largest

b)   1.4   5.3   8.7   3.5   1.5

[ ]   [ ]   [ ]   [ ]   [ ]

largest   smallest

3. Write these fractions as decimals.

a) three tenths [ ]   **b)** one and a tenth [ ]   **c)** four and five tenths [ ]

4. Change these pence into pounds (£).

a) 146p [ ]   **b)** 318p [ ]   **c)** 566p [ ]   **d)** 105p [ ]

5. Make the corners add up to the middle number.

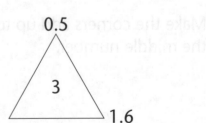

1.2   0.5

3   3

1.3   1.6

 Draw more triangles. Make the corners add up to 4 using decimal numbers.

developing **Numeracy Skills**

✦ **Where do they go?** ✦

1. Write where these numbers go on the line.

| 4.3 | 3.9 | 1.7 | 0.9 | 2.1 | 2.8 | 4.7 |

```
|₁₁₁₁|₁₁₁₁|₁₁₁₁|₁₁₁₁|₁₁₁₁|
0       1       2       3       4       5
```

2. Put these numbers in order.

a)   10.1   6.5   5.3   8.7   6.4

smallest   largest

b)   £8.90   87p   £10.01   347p   £1.01

largest   smallest

3. Write these fractions as decimals.

a) seven tenths [ ]   **b)** six and a tenth [ ]   **c)** eight and five tenths [ ]

4. Convert into pounds (£).

a) 104p [ ]   **b)** 501p [ ]   **c)** 1678p [ ]   **d)** 800p [ ]

5. Make the sum of the corner numbers equal to the 10 in the centre.

1.2 ┌────── 3.5   4.1 ┌──────
    │   10   │   │   10   │
    └────── 2.4   └────── 1.7

 Draw some more squares. Write 4 decimal numbers in the corners that add up to 10.

Reasoning about numbers

 Overall learning objectives

✦ Choose appropriate number operations and methods for calculations.
✦ Explain methods and reasoning about numbers orally and in writing.
✦ Solve mathematical problems or puzzles.
✦ Make and investigate general statements.
✦ Explain relationships in words.

LESSON ONE
HOW CAN THIS BE DONE?

 Assessment focus

Can the children solve mathematical problems and explain their methods?

 Oral work and mental calculation

Doubling and halving

✦ Give the children some doubling and halving problems requiring a rapid response.
✦ *"I had £45 for my birthday and spent half on a pair of shoes. How much is left?"*
✦ *"Suzie drank half a litre of milk. How many millilitres was this?"*
✦ *"A recipe makes 48 little cakes. How many cakes will double the mixture make?"*
✦ *"I wanted to make a shelf. I had some wood that measured 135cm. I needed twice as much, so how much wood must I buy?"*

 Starting point: whole class

✦ Draw this 'dartboard' on the board.
✦ Explain that like a real game, three 'darts' are used each time and darts can land on the same number. Make this into a game by getting three children to throw a dice. Write the three numbers and add the score. Repeat this a few more times,

before asking the children the following questions:
✦ *"Which is the highest number that can be made?"*
✦ *"Which is the lowest number?"*
✦ *"Which numbers in between can be made?"*
✦ *"Can some numbers be made in more than one way?"*
✦ Now draw a circle around the outside and say that any darts landing here will score double points. Practise saying the doubles of the numbers and asking questions such as *"What is the highest score now?"*
✦ Tell the groups that they will all be working on similar boards.

 Group activities

 Focus group

Display this dartboard. The grey area represents doubles. Practise saying the doubles of all the numbers, then adding pairs of numbers mentally before moving on to adding three numbers to make scores. Ask the children to find ways of scoring 100. Discuss the strategies they might need to use. Try finding one way together before the group begins to work in pairs to find the possible ways to score 100. Change the score to 75 and ask the group to find this in different ways. Which score has the most possibilities?

Teacher-independent groups

Activity sheet 1: This sheet contains the dartboard from the starter session. Encourage the children to work systematically to find all the possible scores they can make on the dartboard and also to look for the most frequently occurring score. Suggest they use interlocking cubes if necessary.

Activity sheet 2: This dartboard has eight sections which means there are more possible scores. The group is challenged to find as many ways as possible of making particular scores. Again, systematic working will help with finding solutions.

Reasoning about numbers

Activity sheet 3: This group works with a similar dartboard to that on Activity sheet 2, except that it includes doubles that enable higher scores to be made and there are a greater number of options for making the scores.

◆ ◆ ◆ ◆ ◆ ◆

 LESSON TWO
WHAT'S THE RULE?

◆ Assessment focus

Can the children make general statements and describe what they have done?

◆ Resources

✦ 0–9 number cards
✦ large 0–100 number line
✦ multiplication squares

◆ Oral work and mental calculation

Number investigation

✦ Draw this on the board:

 + □ = □

✦ Tell the children to use the digits 1–9 and to find as many ways as possible of filling the boxes. After a few minutes share what they have done.

◆ Plenary session

✦ Ask pairs of children from each group to explain to the class how they made one of their target scores and any reasoning they used in deciding on the numbers to make the total. Discuss whether there were any other ways this might have been done. Which might be the most important digits in a number to consider when finding a total?
✦ Talk about facts they used that they knew and those they needed to work out, possibly using paper jottings, a number line or a 100 square.

◆ ◆ ◆ ◆ ◆ ◆

◆ Starting point: whole class

✦ Together find pairs of numbers that make 15. Give the number 5 and, using their 0–9 cards, the children show the other number to make 15. Repeat this with other pairs of numbers that equal 15. Continue by giving 2 numbers and asking which third number will make 15, for example *"I have 4 and 3. What other number do I need to make 15?"* As they find the trios of numbers write them on the board.
✦ Draw this diagram on the board. Tell group 1 that they will be working with a picture like this. They will be arranging the numbers 1–9 in the circles so that each line of 3 circles totals 15.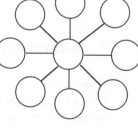
✦ Show groups 2 and 3 the diagrams they will be using for arranging their numbers.

◆ Group activities

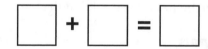 Focus group

Revise odd and even numbers with this group, writing some on a large sheet of paper. Ask them to

Reasoning about numbers

choose two odd numbers and add them. *"Is the answer odd or even? Did everyone find the same thing?"* Check by adding two more odd numbers. Go on to adding two even numbers. What is the answer this time – odd or even? What if they add an odd and an even number? Let them continue by adding different combinations of odd and even numbers and writing the strings on the paper as generalisations: ODD + EVEN = ODD, EVEN + EVEN = EVEN, ODD + ODD = EVEN. Make sure that several examples of each combination are worked to test the hypotheses.

Teacher-independent groups

Group 1: Following on from the starter, this group should make each set of three circles total 15, using the numbers 1–9. As the centre number is common to all the lines, some thought needs to be given to the best number. If they experience difficulty you might like to suggest they choose the middle number (5) of the 9 they are working with and write that in the centre. When that problem is solved, they can work with another run of nine consecutive numbers, such as 5–13 and apply the same strategy.

Group 2: Provide this group with copies of this square. They have to arrange the numbers 1–8 along the sides of the square so that each side totals 13 and try to discover whether

there is only one way this can be done. They can continue by trying to make the sides total 14 in different ways, using some of the strategies they used for the first part of the activity.

Group 3: Make copies of this diagram for this group. They have to put the numbers 1–9 along the sides of the triangle to make them add to 20. You might like to suggest that a strategy is to place the middle three numbers of the run in the corners. Extend the activity by asking if they can make other equal totals along each side, such as 21 or 19.

◆ *Plenary session*

◆ Ask a pair from each group to explain their strategy for solving a particular problem. Let other children working on the same problem say whether they had worked in a different way.

◆ The children from the focus group can explain some of the things they found about adding odd and even numbers. These can be written as if they were codes, such as O + E + O = E. The children have to suggest some possible numbers for the code to test the theory.

◆ *Further activities*

◆ Draw a brick wall and write the numbers 1–5 along the bottom row. Pairs of numbers are added to make the number that goes in the bricks above until the top is reached. In this example the number at the top is 48.

◆ By changing the position of the numbers 1–5 along the bottom row the children can explore what other numbers they get at the top.

◆ *Extension*

◆ Using the brick wall expect generalisations about the best arrangement of the numbers 1–5 to get the highest/lowest total at the top.

◆ *Support*

◆ Use a simpler version of the brick wall with only three or four bricks along the bottom.

✦ What's the score? ✦

Use 3 darts.

What is the lowest score you can make?

What is the highest score you can make?

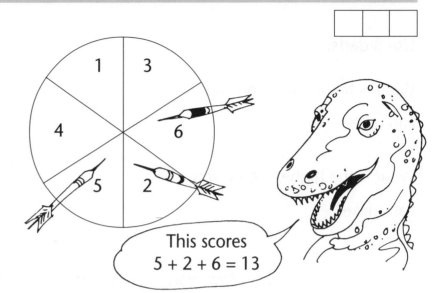

This scores
$5 + 2 + 6 = 13$

Write as many scores as you can make between the highest and the lowest.

What score did you make in the most ways?

 Find some ways to do this. ☐ + ☐ + 3 = ☐ + ☐

69

◆ **What's the score?** ◆

Use 3 darts.

What is the lowest score you can make?

What is the highest score you can make?

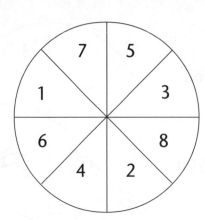

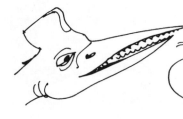

How many different ways can you make a score of 16?

How many ways can you score 20?

Find some other scores you can make.

 Find some ways to do this. ___ + ___ + 30 = ___ + ___

developing
**Numeracy
Skills**

✦ **What's the score?** ✦

Use 3 darts.

What is the lowest score you can make?

What is the highest score you can make?

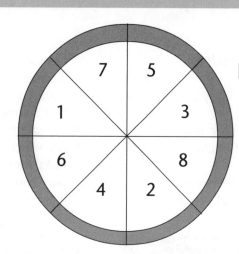

= doubles

How many different ways can you make a score of 30?

How many ways can you score 25?

Make as many scores between the highest and the lowest as you can.

 Find some ways to do this. ____ + ____ + 300 = ____ + ____

Photocopiable

71

Measures – 1

 Overall learning objectives

- ◆ Use, read and write the vocabulary related to length, area and perimeter.
- ◆ Use metric units and their abbreviations.
- ◆ Know relationships between familiar units and convert metric units.
- ◆ Solve problems related to measurement.
- ◆ Measure and calculate area and perimeter.

LESSON ONE MEASURING UP

 Assessment focus

Can the children use linear measuring equipment with increasing accuracy?

 Resources

- ◆ linear measuring equipment – tape measures, rulers, surveyor's tapes, trundle wheels, height measure, callipers and so on

 Oral work and mental calculation

Addition and subtraction facts to 20

- ◆ Give the children practice with quick recall of addition and subtraction facts to 20. Write some examples on the board. Tell them that they have two minutes to write as many facts as they can. (A less able group can work with numbers to 10 within the time limit.) When time is up, the children can write the facts on the board.
- ◆ Give another number under 20, allowing a short time for writing its addition and subtraction facts.

 Starting point: whole class

- ◆ Display a range of linear measuring equipment, including callipers. Hold up an item and ask the children what units it uses and what they might

measure with it. Check that they know where to measure from with a ruler and how to read the scale. Focus on millimetres by asking if they can find 56mm.
- ◆ Repeat this with other equipment.
- ◆ Ask which equipment would be used for specific tasks, for example to measure height, or the playground, or the top of a drawing pin. Show them a ball and ask how they could find by measuring if it will go through a hole. Demonstrate the use of callipers for this purpose.
- ◆ Write up some equivalent measures.
  1cm = 10mm, 2cm = 20mm, and so on.
  1m = 100cm = 1000mm, 1cm = 0.01m
  1mm = 0.001m
  Leave these on the board to help the groups as they work. Give them some numbers to be converted between metric units and write up both versions, such as 6cm = 60mm, 16cm = 0.16m and so on.

 Group activities

 Focus group

Assess the children's ability to use equipment accurately and select the best units for a task. Tell them that they are to work in pairs to test the theory that 3 times the measurement around a person's head is equal to their height. Discuss which equipment to use and its units of measurement. Give them time to talk about their methods. For example, will they measure around their heads and multiply by 3, then check their heights? As they work, watch and check their level of accuracy. Can they convert the measurements to other units?

 Teacher-independent groups

Activity sheet 1: This sheet asks the children to measure model dinosaurs to the nearest centimetre, recording in centimetres and millimetres. The personal measurements are taken in centimetres and also recorded as metres.

Activity sheet 2: This sheet is similar to Activity sheet 1, except that the children have to do some

Measures – 1

calculations and given lengths include half centimetres.

Activity sheet 3: This sheet asks the children to measure given lengths to the nearest millimetre. Some children may suggest measuring the models with string to find the difference between the picture of the model and the length taking the tail into consideration. Other calculations include division and rounding to the nearest centimetre. It is suggested that calculators are used.

LESSON TWO
INSIDE AND OUTSIDE

Assessment focus

Can the children measure and calculate area and perimeter, then make generalisations about them?

Resources

+ interlocking cubes and squares
+ squared paper (1cm, 2cm and 4cm)
+ lolly sticks (or other short sticks)
+ 10p coins

Oral work and mental calculation

Mental subtraction of small numbers

+ Play 'Pass it round' with the whole class. Choose a starting number, for example 50. Tell the children that, in turn, they must subtract either 2 or 3 from it and then from the number that is left, for example: 50 – 3 = 47 – 2 = 45 – 2 = 43 and so on. Someone could write the numbers on the board as you go. The winner is the person who subtracts 2 or 3 to leave 1. Let the children play the game in groups. Discuss strategies for winning.

Plenary session

+ Ask the groups to explain the units they used for their measuring activities. *"How did you measure across your thumb?"*
+ Group 1 can share whether an 8.6 metre dinosaur would fit into the classroom and how they found out.
+ Ask the other groups to share the problems and their solutions.
+ Discuss the importance of both accurate measurement and estimation.

Starting point: whole class

+ On a large sheet of 4cm squared paper, draw some different sized rectangles. Explain that the outside of a rectangle is called the perimeter and show how it is measured like any other line. Demonstrate how the perimeter encloses the squares and ask how the space inside the rectangle, the area, could be measured. Show them how it is measured in squares. Make the link with multiplication. Say that each group will be given a perimeter length to work with and they will make as many rectangles as they can with it, then find the area.

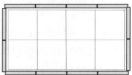

+ Demonstrate making perimeters using short sticks and recording this on squared paper.
+ *"Do you think identical perimeters will give the same area?"*

Group activities

    Focus group

Provide these children with 20 short sticks each. Tell them they will be drawing plans to make a run for a pet rabbit using 20 pieces of 'fencing' a metre long.

Measures – 1

The fencing can only be joined at right angles or in straight lines. Let everyone make a closed shape using all the sticks. Share what everyone has done and ask which will give the rabbit most room to play. Tell them to record their shapes on squared paper and write the area. As they are working, talk about shapes with the greatest area. Can they explain possible reasons?

 Teacher-independent groups

Group 1: Give these children 20 short sticks each and tell them to make as many different rectangles as they can and to record them by drawing on squared paper. Ask them to count the squares to find the area and see if they are all the same.

Group 2: This group uses a perimeter of 24cm to draw different rectangles on squared paper. Encourage systematic work to ensure all the possibilities are found. The area of each rectangle is found by counting squares. Ask the children to write comments about the areas and reasons for the differences.

Group 3: Working with a perimeter of 40cm, this group explores the different rectangles that can be made. Rectangles are drawn on squared paper and areas found either by multiplication or counting squares. Ask for generalisations about why the same perimeter does not necessarily result in the same area. They might notice that rectangles closest to a square have a greater area.

◆ *Plenary session*

✦ Ask one or two children to show and explain their work. How can areas of rectangles be calculated rather than by counting squares? Demonstrate how multiplication can be used and practise some examples. Refer to the prediction made in the introduction about links between area and perimeter to find out if they were right.

◆ *Further activities*

✦ Investigate relationships between the measurements of other parts of the body, for example how many digits measure the same as a foot?

✦ Develop an understanding of conservation of area through the use of tangram puzzles. Ask the children to rearrange the 7 pieces to make a picture.

 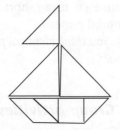

✦ A pentomino is made by joining 5 squares along at least one side. Investigate the different ways this can be done. Find the perimeter of each one (see opposite).

◆ *Extension*

✦ Measure a 10p coin in mm or cm and mm (approximately 24mm). Using just the one coin or its measurement can the children calculate the length, width and area of a small book? They could make a 'ruler' measuring in 10p units or use multiples of 24.

◆ *Support*

✦ Give these children a length of string to measure. They use this to enclose the largest possible area on squared paper.

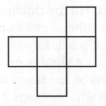

Area = 5 squares
Perimeter = 12 units

Area = 5 squares
Perimeter = 10 units

developing **Numeracy Skills**

✦ **Measuring up** ✦

1. Measure the model dinosaurs in cm and mm.

a)

length

height

length = ☐ cm or ☐ mm

height = ☐ cm or ☐ mm

b)

height

length

length = ☐ cm or ☐ mm

height = ☐ cm or ☐ mm

2. Write your measurements in cm and in m and cm.

My height is ☐ cm or ☐ m and ☐ cm.

My full arm span is ☐ cm or ☐ m and ☐ cm.

Which measurement is longer? ☐

How do you know?

3. Match these to the units you would use.

a flea

a door

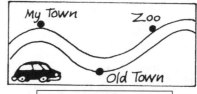

a coin

| kilometres and metres | millimetres | centimetres and millimetres | metres and centimetres |

A dinosaur measures 8.6m long. Is this longer
or shorter than your classroom? Write what
you did to find out.

developing
Numeracy
Skills

✦ **Measuring up** ✦

1. Measure the model dinosaurs in cm and mm.

a)

length

height

length = ☐ cm or ☐ mm

height = ☐ cm or ☐ mm

b)

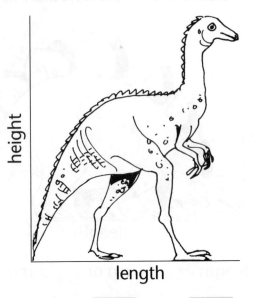

height

length

length = ☐ cm or ☐ mm

height = ☐ cm or ☐ mm

2. Using 2 different units of measurement, measure:

your
digit

your
hand

your
cubit

My digit ☐ ☐   My hand ☐ ☐   My cubit ☐ ☐

3. Measure your height and full arm span. Record using 2 different units.

My height ☐ ☐

My arm span ☐ ☐

The difference is ☐ ☐

Which is greater – your height or your arm span? ☐

Measure your foot and your handspan. Find the
difference in mm and cm. Write what you did.

Photocopiable

©Hopscotch Educational Publishing

✦ Measuring up ✦

1. Measure the model dinosaurs in cm and mm.

a)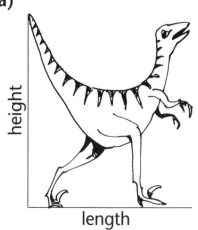

height

length

Write them as cm and mm.

length = [ ] cm or [ ] mm

height = [ ] cm or [ ] mm

b)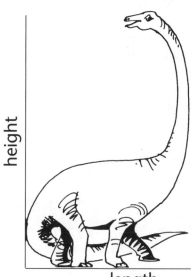

height

length

length = [ ] cm or [ ] mm

height = [ ] cm or [ ] mm

2. Using 2 different units of measurement, measure:

your
face   ←——→

My face [ ] [ ]

your
smile   ←—→

My smile [ ] [ ]

around →
your
head

My head [ ] [ ]

Which was longest? [   ]   shortest? [   ]

What is the difference? [   ]

3. Measure your height and handspan to the nearest cm.

My height = [   ] cm   My handspan = [   ] cm

Find how many handspans tall you are to the nearest whole number.

   Measure your thumb width and your foot length. How many
thumbs long is your foot? Show how you worked it out.

Measures – 2

◆ Overall learning objectives

+ Solve problems involving measurement.
+ Suggest suitable units and measuring equipment to estimate or measure length, mass, capacity and time.
+ Record estimates and readings from scales to a suitable degree of accuracy.
+ Read the time from a range of clocks and solve problems involving time.

◆ LESSON ONE ◆
HOW DO WE MEASURE THIS?

◆ Assessment focus

Can the children use a variety of capacity measuring equipment and read different capacity scales?

◆ Resources

+ a collection of boxes and plastic bottles
+ measuring cylinders and jugs
+ a collection of cups and mugs
+ sand, rice, water etc.
+ 1cm squared card and paper
+ interlocking cubes and centicubes

◆ Oral work and mental calculation

Partitioning to add several numbers

+ Write the alphabet on the board and assign a number to each letter. Use 1–26. The children have to find the value of their name. For example, Adam is 19 (1 + 4 + 1 + 13). Children with shorter names could also find the value of their surnames. Ask those with longer names to explain their method for finding their value.
+ On their tables the children should then try to add all the name values to find the 'most valuable group'. Order the values of the people in a group. Find the difference between the highest and lowest.

◆ Starting point: whole class

+ Display the collection of boxes and bottles. Ask the children to suggest ways of finding how much each contains and the units they would use to measure this. Show them a litre bottle and ask if they can remember the capacity.
+ Talk about centilitres and millilitres as smaller units of a litre. Write up: 1 litre = 100 centilitres = 1000 millilitres.
+ Show a selection of measuring jugs and cylinders, letting the children handle them and talk about the scales. *"Which would be most appropriate for measuring small/large amounts?"* Write some capacity measurements on the board and discuss how to convert from one unit to another using decimals, for example 650ml = 0.650 litres.

◆ Group activities

 Focus group

Use a collection of different sized cups and mugs, a selection of different sized cylinders and measuring jugs with an assortment of scales. Hold up one cup and say *"If I fill this with water which measure will I use?"* Find its capacity using measuring containers with different scales and discuss which is best. Let the group work in pairs to find the capacity of all the cups, measuring each one with different scales. Record the capacities in litres, centilitres and millilitres. Finally, they could arrange the cups and mugs in capacity order.

 Teacher-independent groups

Group 1: Give this group a selection of small boxes and measuring containers. Ask them to work in pairs and find the capacity of each one, using sand and then rice. They check that both give the same reading.

Group 2: Working in pairs, one of a pair makes a 3 x 3 x 3 cube from 1cm squared card and the other a 6 x 6 x 6 cube. They find the capacities and record them, then compare by finding the difference in capacity. How many times more does the larger

Measures – 2

container hold? What about the next size? (Note: doubling the dimensions gives 8 times the capacity.)

Group 3: Using 1cm squared card, pairs of children start with 11 x 11 squares and make a set of 5 open boxes by cutting off increasingly large squares from the corners and folding up. Estimate the greatest capacity and test.

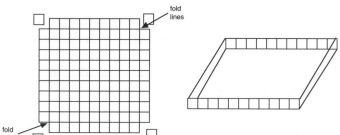

fold lines

fold lines

✦ *Plenary session*

✦ Representatives from each group should share their findings and methods of working.

✦ *"What have you learned about capacity during this lesson?"*

✦ LESSON TWO HOW MUCH TIME?

✦ *Assessment focus*

Can the children read different clocks and solve problems involving time?

✦ *Resources*

✦ clocks – analogue, digital and stop clocks
✦ a number line
✦ copies of TV programmes for one day

✦ *Oral work and mental calculation*

Mixed calculations

✦ Put a number line or 100 square on display. Tell the children to listen very carefully because you are going to give a starting number, followed by two or more calculations to be done in their heads as you say them. Give easy examples initially, to

ensure involvement of the less able, such as *"What is 6, add 10, add 4, subtract 2?"*

✦ Include calculations with 100s, such as *"What is 200 + 300 + 20 – 1?"* or *"What is 35 x 10 – 20?"*

✦ The numbers can be written up after the children have answered and methods discussed.

✦ *Starting point: whole class*

✦ Point to the class clock (or show the present time on a demonstration clock). Remind the children about counting around the clock in 5-minute intervals and that there are 60 minutes in an hour. Ask what the time is to the nearest 5 minutes, then the nearest minute. Invite someone to write the time on the board using a digital display. Say *"When is it playtime? How long is that to wait?"* Can the children show how to work this out? Demonstrate on a clock how to add first hours and then minutes.

✦ Discuss different ways of reading the time, such as 29 minutes past 3 is the same as 31 minutes before 4 o'clock.

✦ Pose questions about time for the children to solve, such as *"A museum opens at 9.30am and*

Measures – 2

closes at 5.15pm For how long is it open?" Talk about strategies for finding answers.

Group activities

Focus group

Give pairs of children a copy of the timetable for the day's television programmes. Ask questions about it, such as *"What could I watch at 7 o'clock this evening? How long will the programme last?"* and *"At what times of the day could I watch the news? How long is that altogether?"* Ask the children to suggest other questions about the timetable and find answers together. Assess their ability to read and write the time. In pairs they write three questions about the times of television programmes using the information from the timetable. The questions are then shared, discussed and answered orally.

Teacher-independent groups

Activity Sheet 1: Continuing from the starter activity, this sheet asks the children to read and write the times given on the clocks and then write times using digital and analogue displays. The times are written to the nearest five minutes. Make small clocks available for reference. Practical timing activities give the opportunity to measure time in

seconds and to compare their results with those of others.

Activity Sheet 2: These activities are similar to those on Activity sheet 1, except that the children have to read and write the time to the nearest minute. The practical timing activity requires the calculation of differences between the time taken by two group members for a task.

Activity Sheet 3: This is similar to Activity sheet 2 except that for the practical activity the children count the number of times it is repeated in one minute and use that information to calculate the possible number of repeats in an hour.

Plenary session

✦ The groups can tell the class about their timed activities. Group 3 can explain how they worked out the number of cubes they could fit together in an hour, based on the number joined in one minute. Ask group 2 how to calculate the number of times they could write their name in 10 minutes. Find out from group 1 who fitted 20 cubes together in the shortest/longest time and how to find the difference between them. Conclude by discussing when, during the day, they need to solve problems linked to time and what these might be.

Further activities

✦ Make a small open box using cm squared card. How many centicubes will it hold? How many millilitres of sand?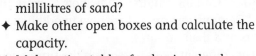

✦ Make other open boxes and calculate the capacity.

✦ Make a timetable of a day in school, calculating the time spent doing different activities. Extend this to a 24-hour period.

Extension

✦ Use a litre bottle and plastic cup to calculate how many cups of a drink could be poured. How many bottles are needed to give a drink to everyone in the class – or the school?

✦ Make timetables of a day/week in school, calculating the time spent doing different activities.

Support

✦ Make open boxes from 2cm squared paper to hold 18 interlocking cubes.

✦ What time? ✦

1. Draw the hands to show the time.

a)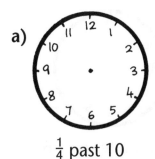

$\frac{1}{4}$ past 10

b)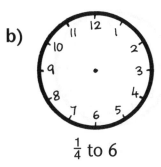

$\frac{1}{4}$ to 6

c)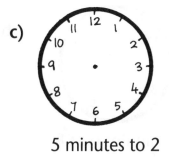

5 minutes to 2

2. What's the time?

a)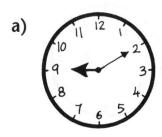

_____

b)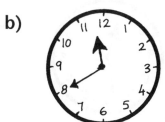

_____

c)

_____

3. Write the times on the digital clocks.

a) 10 minutes past 1   b) 25 minutes past 7   c) 55 minutes past 8

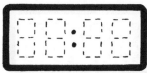      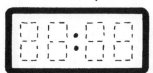

4. Class 4 went to the Dinosaur Museum. They arrived at 9.30am.
   They left at 12.45pm. They arrived back at school at 1.30pm.

   a) How long did they stay? _____

   b) How long was the journey back? _____

 Use a second-timer. Work with a partner. How long does it take to:
a) Write your name 10 times?   b) Fit 20 cubes together?
Who was quicker?

Name _____

✦ What time? ✦

1. Draw the hands to show the time.

a)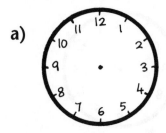

20 minutes past 8

b)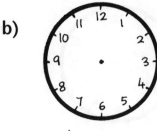

$\frac{1}{4}$ to 11

c)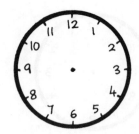

12 minutes past 6

2. Write the time shown on these clocks.

a)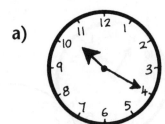

b)

c)

_____   _____   _____

3. Write the times on the digital clocks.

a) $\frac{1}{4}$ to 6   b) 25 minutes past 10   c) 5 minutes to 4

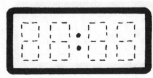   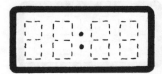   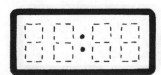

4. Class 4 went to the Dinosaur Museum. The bus journey took 35 minutes. They arrived at 10.45am and stayed for $2\frac{3}{4}$ hours.

   a) What time did they leave school?

   b) What time did they leave the museum?

 Use a stopwatch. Work with a partner. How long does it take you both to make a 4 x 4 square with cubes? Who was faster? What was the difference in the time it took you?

developing
Numeracy
Skills

✦ **What time?** ✦

1. Draw the hands on the clocks to show the times.

a) 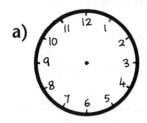   b) 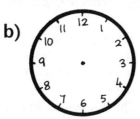   c) 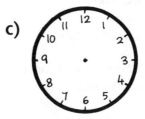   d)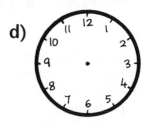

     8.39am   54 minutes past 3   26 minutes to 1   13 minutes to 4

2. What is the time difference?

a) 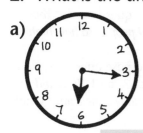      b)

3. Class 4 went to the Dinosaur Museum. The bus left school at 9.35am. The journey took 50 minutes. What time did it arrive at the museum?

4. This is the timetable for the museum visit.

   a) How long did the class stay?

   b) How long did they work and listen to the talk?

   c) What time did they get back to school?

> 10.30 – 10.45 video
> 10.45 – 11.00 break
> 11.00 – 12.10 tour museum
>   and work
> 12.10 – 12.25 talk
> 12.30 – return to school

5. Use a second-timer and work with a partner.

   a) How many cubes can you fit together in 10 seconds?

   b) How many is this in one minute?   one hour?

   c) How did you work this out?

      How many times can you write your name in 10 seconds?
                              How many in a minute and an hour?

Handling data

◆ Overall learning objectives

◆ Solve problems involving collection, sorting and organisation of data.
◆ Represent data in the form of graphs and charts.
◆ Interpret graphs and charts and make predictions.
◆ Discuss and make predictions using numerical data.

LESSON ONE
BAR CHARTS/PICTOGRAMS

◆ Assessment focus

Can the children extract information from and interpret graphs and tables?

◆ Resources

◆ squared paper
◆ commercially-produced graphs
◆ interlocking cubes
◆ stopwatches
◆ one-minute timers.

◆ Oral work and mental calculation

Multiplication and division

◆ Give practice with the mental recall of multiplication and division facts, using a range of vocabulary.
  "How many 2s in 24?"
  "How many 10s in 50?"
  "What is 36 divided by 9?"
  "What is the product of 10 and 6?" and so on.
◆ Answers should be shown on a count of three using 0–9 cards.
◆ Pose some questions requiring the use of known facts, for example *"What is 4 x 15?"* or *"What is 20 x 9?"* *"How did you work it out?"*

◆ Starting point: whole class

◆ Draw the axes for a graph marking the vertical axis in multiples of 2. Talk about the need for axes to be the right lengths for the amount of data.
◆ Quickly collect data from the class, with questions such as *"What fruit have you brought in your lunchbox today?"* or *"How did you come to school?"* Label the graph and axes, stressing the reasons and importance of this. Draw one bar to represent one part of the data and invite the children to draw the others, asking such questions as *"You have to add an odd number of people, so how high will the bar need to be?"*
◆ Once the graph is completed pose questions, including *"Why do you think...?"* and *"If we did this again tomorrow would the results be the same? What makes you say that?"*

◆ Group activities

 Focus group

Depending on the group's ability, write the numerical data from one of the graphs on the activity sheets. Discuss the amount of data and how it could be grouped to draw a graph. Say that they are to show this as a pictogram. Can they explain what this is? If not demonstrate how data is shown on this type of chart. Let individuals choose the symbol to represent a group of data, such as a book or a person. As they work assess their ability to organise data for easier interpretation, such as symbols lined under each other. Ask what can be learned from the graph, including *"Why do you think there were more book sales/visitors on Saturday than other days?"* and *"Why did you choose multiples of 2 (5 or 10)?"* Focus on the fact that using more data means using larger groupings to make interpretation easier. Show a copy of the relevant graph on the activity sheet and compare them. Which is easier to read and when might each be used? Share commercially-produced graphs (these can often be found in holiday brochures) and charts.

Handling data

Teacher-independent groups

Activity sheet 1: This has a graph to interpret based on the sales of a book at the Dinosaur Museum. The vertical axis is marked in multiples of 2 and the data to be added to the graph is an odd number.

Activity sheet 2: This data is grouped in 5s because larger numbers are involved.

Activity sheet 3: This activity requires the children to interpret data grouped in 10s.

◆ Plenary session

✦ Ask representatives from each group to share the most interesting thing they found from their graph. Can they suggest why graphs are used to give information instead of writing it in words, and the use people make of graphs?

LESSON TWO COLLECTING AND REPRESENTING DATA

◆ Assessment focus

Can the children devise a question, collect data and present it appropriately, making interpretations and predictions?

◆ Resources

✦ picture cards
✦ cubes

✦ number cards
✦ see-through containers

◆ Oral work and mental calculation

Multiplication by 9 and 99

✦ Practise counting in 10s to 200 and then 100s, stopping at 1500. Say the 9 times table together, writing it on the board. Tell the class that now they are going to try writing the 99 times table! Write the first two to help the less able. Give a few minutes for the children to make jottings. Ask individuals to come up and write the 99 times

table beside the 9 times table and compare them. Ask them to suggest a quick method for multiplying by 99 (multiply by 100 and subtract ones). Refer to money where prices are given as 99p. Give examples to be calculated.

◆ Starting point: whole class

✦ "How many cubes do you think can be counted in 15 seconds?" Ask everyone to write an estimate. Write some of them on the board. Give each group a large number of cubes and when you say "Go" they count as many cubes as possible until "Time's up". They write down their number.
✦ Groups compare and order scores. Ask:
"Did anyone score more than 50?"
"Who counted the most in your group?"
"How did you group the cubes?"
✦ Compare the totals with the estimates and tell the groups they will be drawing graphs of the outcomes from their cube count. Use some of the data provided for group 1 to draw the axes, reminding the children to make sure that all the data can be included. Discuss a possible scale for the vertical axis and write up the multiples of 2 to help group 1.
✦ Tell the children to think about the information the graph gives, to share later.

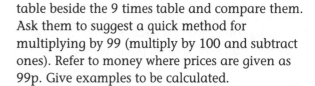

Handling data

◆ Group activities

Focus group

Tell this group they will be finding out about shoe sizes in the class but first they must decide what to find out. Help them make predictions like *"Boys have bigger feet than girls"* or *"Most people in Year 4 wear size 3 shoes"*. Plan a data collection sheet and help to organise the collection effectively. The pairs collect information from each group and pool the data. Ask them to present the data as a graph. Talk about the best type to draw, how to label the axes and show the data. Discuss completed graphs and whether the original question can be answered.

Teacher-independent groups

Group 1: This group should draw a bar graph of their cube count, using a scale of multiples of 2. Suggest centimetre squared paper is used to help draw the scale on the vertical axis and the width of the bars. Ask for written comments about the graph to share.

Group 2: Ask this group to draw their cube count graph using multiples of 5 on the vertical axis. Among the questions they can consider is the total number of cubes they counted.

Group 3: This group presents their data in graph form using multiples of 10 as the scale and showing both the estimate and the actual count for each person. The bars for each person can be compared to find the person with the best estimate.

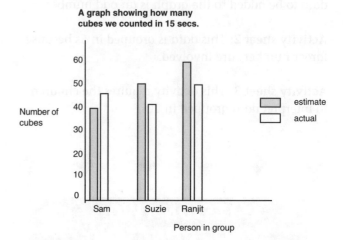

◆ Plenary session

+ Groups share their graphs and some of the information they found. Encourage the class to ask questions for individuals to answer. The focus group share their conclusions about the sizes of shoe worn by the class and why this might be the case.

◆ Further activities

+ Collect graphs showing temperatures, hours of sunshine and so on from holiday brochures. Ask the children to use the data to decide where to spend a holiday both in a sunny and in a cooler place. They should be able give to reasons based on the data for decisions made.

◆ Extension

◆ Keep a record of spellings or tables tests, to show progress.

◆ Support

+ Give practical opportunities for making graphs with cubes, such as 'Which is the most popular colour of car?'

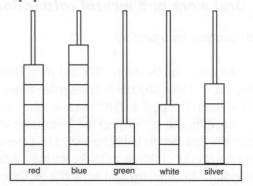

✦ Dinosaur book sales ✦

Sales of dinosaur books

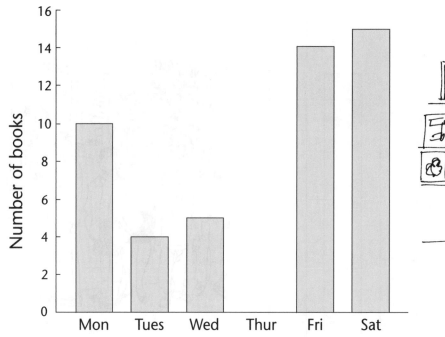

1. Use this chart to draw the bar for Thursday. Finish the chart.

Monday	Tuesday	Wednesday	Thursday	Friday	Saturday
			7		

2. Fewest books were sold on

3. [   ] more books were sold on Friday than on Tuesday.

4. Altogether, [   ] books were sold on Friday and Saturday.

5. Altogether, [   ] books were sold. Write how you worked this out.

_____

   Write 3 more things you can find out from the graph.

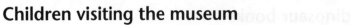

✦ Dinosaur Museum visitors ✦

Children visiting the museum

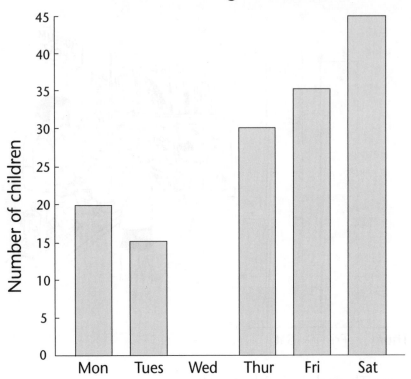

1. On Wednesday, 20 children visited the museum. Draw the bar.

2. Which day was busiest?

   Why do you think it was busiest then? _____

   _____

3. How many more children visited on Saturday than on Tuesday?

4. How many more visited on the last 3 days of the week than the

   first 3 days?

5. How many fewer went on Thursday than on Saturday?

   _____

   Write 3 more things you can read about on the graph.

developing
Numeracy Skills

✦ Dinosaur Museum visitors ✦

Children visiting the museum

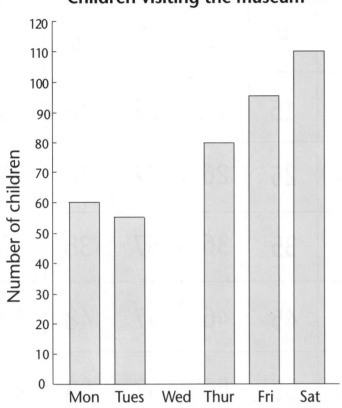

1. On Wednesday there were 15 fewer children than on Monday. Draw the bar.

2. How many children visited on the busiest day?

   Why do you think this was busiest? _____

3. How many fewer children went on Wednesday than on Saturday?

4. How many children visited on Monday and Tuesday?

5. How many more children visited on the last three days than on the

   first three days?

6. Why do you think fewer children went on Wednesday? _____

   _____

Write 3 questions about the graph. Give them to your friend to answer.

◆ 99 square ◆

0	1	2	3	4	5	6	7	8	9
10	11	12	13	14	15	16	17	18	19
20	21	22	23	24	25	26	27	28	29
30	31	32	33	34	35	36	37	38	39
40	41	42	43	44	45	46	47	48	49
50	51	52	53	54	55	56	57	58	59
60	61	62	63	64	65	66	67	68	69
70	71	72	73	74	75	76	77	78	79
80	81	82	83	84	85	86	87	88	89
90	91	92	93	94	95	96	97	98	99

developing
**Numeracy
Skills**

Name _____

 # Blank 99/100 square

Name _____

◆ Finding a way ◆

◆ This is a maze of rooms. In each room there is a number to collect.

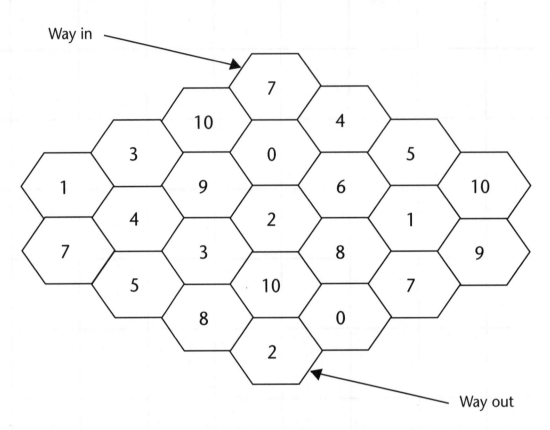

Way in

Way out

◆ Find your way through the maze so that you collect the numbers that will make the largest total. You can only move from Way in to Way out and you can only visit each room once.

◆ Write down the numbers you collect and add them. _____

◆ What is the total? _____

◆ Add the numbers in a different way. What is the total now? _____

◆ Find your way through the maze that will give the smallest total.

◆ Write the numbers and add them. _____

◆ What is the total? _____

◆ Ask your friends what numbers they made. Did you all choose the same way through the maze?

Photocopiable

©Hopscotch Educational Publishing

Name _____

◆ 4 in a row ◆

developing
Numeracy
Skills

Name _____

 # Dinosaur footprint game

Start

Numeracy
Year 4/P5

developing Numeracy Skills

Photocopiable

Name _____

◆ Dinosaur footprint race ◆

Start

 13

 16

 21

 8

 14

17

37

98

72

You need a 1–6 dice.
Play in pairs moving
around the footprints.
Write the numbers
you land on and keep
a running total.
The winner has the
highest score after 5
minutes.

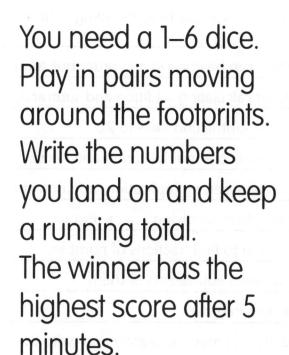

16

27

33

15

51

64

38

4

6

Name _____

✦ Self-assessment sheet ✦

Date

I can… read and write numbers to 10 000	
add or subtract 1, 10, 100 or 1000 to or from whole numbers to 10 000	
multiply and divide whole numbers by 10	
partition numbers into thousands, hundreds, tens and ones	
compare and order a set of numbers	
round whole numbers to the nearest 10, 100 or 1000	
recognise and extend number sequences, including counting back beyond zero	
understand that addition can be done in any order but subtraction cannot	
use different methods for calculating addition and subtraction	
recall all the addition and subtraction facts to 20	
use facts that I know to work out multiplication and division problems	
explain the relationship between multiplication, addition and division	
explain how I solved problems involving +, −, x and ÷	
explain how to use division to find fractions of numbers	
write fractions and find some equivalents of them	
put decimals and fractions in order	
measure length, capacity and mass accurately and write the measurements using decimals	
solve problems involving time	
use multiplication to calculate area and perimeter	
draw, read and interpret bar graphs and tables	
collect data to answer a question and present it to help me make predictions	
I can…	
I can…	
I can…	

developing
Numeracy
Skills

Photocopiable